Bluebeard

A pantomime

Paul Reakes

Samuel French — London
New York - Toronto - Hollywood

ISBN 0 573 16450 9

Please see page iv for further copyright information

CHARACTERS

Mr Rockbottom
Ruby Rockbottom, his daughter
Flora Rockbottom, his daughter
Fetch
Carrie } his servants
Robin Reliant
Baron Bluebeard
Lurkin, his "hunch" man
Mrs Shivers, his housekeeper
Marie, a French kitchen-maid
A Butcher
The Shape, a ghost
Chorus of Townsfolk, Children, Tradespeople, Peasants, Kitchen Staff, Servants, Troubadours, Bats and Brides

COPYRIGHT INFORMATION

(See also page ii)

SYNOPSIS OF SCENES

ACT I

Scene 1	Outside Rockbottom's house
Scene 2	A room in Rockbottom's house
Scene 3	A wood near Bluebeard's castle
Scene 4	A passage in Bluebeard's castle
Scene 5	The castle kitchens

ACT II

Scene 1	The hall of Bluebeard's castle
Scene 2	The passage
Scene 3	Rockbottom's bedroom
Scene 4	The passage
Scene 5	The Black Tower
Scene 6	Before We Go
Scene 7	The Finale

MUSICAL NUMBERS

(See Copyright Notice p.86)

ACT I

No. 1	**Song and Dance**	Chorus and Dancers
No. 2	**Romantic Duet**	Robin and Flora
No. 3	**Comedy Song**	Ruby
No. 4	**Song and Dance**	Fetch, Carrie and Rockbottom
No. 4a	**Reprise of Song 1**	Chorus and Dancers
No. 5	**Song and Dance**	Chorus and Dancers
No. 5a	**Reprise of Song 5**	Chorus and Dancers
No. 6	**Comedy Duet**	Bluebeard and Lurkin
No. 7	**Song and Dance**	Chorus and Dancers
No. 8	**Song and Dance**	Principals, Chorus and Dancers

ACT II

No. 9	**Song and Dance, Romantic Duet**	Chorus and Dancers, Robin and Flora
No. 10	**Comedy Song and Dance**	Ruby, Lurkin and Shivers
No. 11	**Song and Dance**	Marie and Lurkin
No. 12	**Dance**	Dancers
No. 13	**Song and Dance**	Principals, Chorus and Dancers
No. 14	**House Song**	Ruby, Fetch, Carrie and Audience
No. 15	**Finale Song or Reprise**	All

CHARACTERS AND COSTUMES

Mr Rockbottom is a once-prosperous factory owner who has fallen on hard times and is reduced to hiding from his creditors. A robust, likeable character involved in plenty of comic business and audience participation. The part is written to be played with a North Country accent, but this is not essential. His once fine clothes are now shabby and threadbare.

Ruby Rockbottom (Dame) is his elder daughter. Large, loud and ludicrous, she is always on friendly terms with the audience and never misses an opportunity of involving them. At all times her make-up and costumes are outrageous and comical. Apart from her everyday outfits, she gets to wear a travelling costume, an evening gown, a nightdress or pyjama suit. Special Finale costume.

Flora Rockbottom (Principal Girl) is her beautiful and charming young sister. She is never soppy or simpering and shows a strong spirit when standing up to the odious Bluebeard. A good singing voice and dancing ability is called for. She looks delightful in all her costumes, including a travelling outfit, evening gown and nightdress. Finale costume.

Fetch and **Carrie** are Rockbottom's long-suffering but loyal servants. Always on friendly terms with the audience, they are a likeable pair involved in lots of comic business and participation. The parts are written to be played as a male and female duo, (Fetch male), but could be an all-male or all-female partnership. Carrie is the dopey one! Singing and dancing ability an advantage. Apart from their dilapidated servant costumes, they both get to wear a full suit of armour! Finale costumes.

Robin Reliant (Principal Boy) is a handsome, heroic young fellow with a pleasing personality and a great pair of legs! He loves Flora and will do anything to ensure her safety. A strong singing voice and dancing ability are called for. He gets to wear a natty rustic costume and a splendid Troubadour outfit. Finale costume.

Baron Bluebeard is a villain in the best melodrama tradition. He never misses an opportunity of goading the audience into a frenzy of boos and hisses. He can turn on the "oily charm", but mostly he is pompous, overbearing and vicious. He is always magnificently attired in rich robes and turbans, giving him a mysterious Eastern appearance. A slight, indefinable accent would not be out of place. Of course, his most striking feature is an elaborate and curiously coiffured blue beard!

Lurkin is Bluebeard's servant and worshipper. Obviously a dead ringer for Quasimodo, he is hunchbacked, ugly and shambling. He has a thatch of unkempt hair, crooked teeth and a mis-shapen nose. A make-up artist's dream — or nightmare! Although he worships Bluebeard and is utterly repulsive, his comic antics and remarks make him almost loveable. A character part that should be played for maximum comic effect. He only possesses one outfit, and this consists of a ragged tunic with a wide belt and a pair of darned tights which show off his bandy, mis-shapen legs.

Mrs Shivers is Bluebeard's sinister housekeeper. She is definitely a member of the Addams Family, and is probably a close friend of Count Dracula! A tall, gaunt individual with a bloodless face, hollow eyes and purple lips. Her black hair is parted in the middle and drawn back into a severe bun. She wears a long dress of unrelieved black that sweeps the floor as she moves with a strange gliding motion. Not someone you would wish to meet in a dark corridor! However, Mrs Shivers is not what she seems! She is, in fact — Jemima Blond! A Special Agent working undercover to investigate Bluebeard's evil doings. When the disguise comes off, she reveals a mane of luscious blonde hair and a stunning figure clad in a slinky black catsuit and boots. A versatile and competent player is needed for these two very different roles.

Marie is a kitchen-maid at Bluebeard's castle. She is young, very pretty and has a delightful French accent. Despite being rather timid she is a great help when it comes to foiling Bluebeard's evil plans. Singing and dancing ability is called for. She looks perfectly charming in her maid's outfit with cap and apron, etc. Finale costume.

The Butcher is a loud, overbearing individual wearing a striped apron and straw boater. He only appears in Act I, Scene 1, and could double for the Shape.

The Shape only appears in Act II, Scene 3, wearing a black hooded monk's habit and gruesome skull mask.

The Chorus, Dancers and Children appear as Townsfolk, Tradespeople, Villagers, Kitchen Staff, Troubadours, Bats and Bluebeard's Brides. All participate in the action and musical numbers with costumes appropriate to their calling. The Brides (as many as you can muster!) are dressed in picturesque, colourful costumes of many countries.

PRODUCTION NOTES

STAGING

The pantomime offers opportunities for elaborate staging, but can be produced quite simply if facilities and funds are limited.

There are five full sets:

Outside Rockbottom's house
A wood near Bluebeard's castle
The castle kitchens
The hall of Bluebeard's castle
The Black Tower

There is one inset scene:

Rockbottom's bedroom

All these scenes are interlinked with tabs or two frontcloth scenes:

A room in Rockbottom's house
A passage in Bluebeard's castle

There can be a special Finale setting or one of the full set scenes can be used.

The Bed and The Chest
These should be custom built as one unit. Both must be high enough to enable characters to crawl underneath and out again with sufficient ease. The bed needs to be as wide as an ordinary double bed, but its length will be determined by the space available. At the head end, a low opening in the back wall flat allows access under the bed, and into the chest at its foot. The lid of the chest should open towards the audience, thus obscuring the opening from view. The whole construction needs to be strong as it has to take the weight of several people at a time. Please have these pieces of furniture well in use before the actual performance.

LIGHTING AND EFFECTS

Act I is fairly straightforward. There needs to be sinister lighting for the castle scenes and smoke billows from the oven in the kitchen scene. Act II has all the special effects! There are lots of lightning flashes and rolls of thunder. These can be taped, but as they occur so frequently (at every mention of "The Black Tower"!), I would strongly advice the use of a good old fashioned thunder sheet in the wings. There is good opportunity for some spooky lighting in the bedroom scene and during the bats' dance. This number would be greatly enhanced by well-controlled ground mist.

The Cake Making Routine

The actual comic business is left to the individual director. Lots of messy fun with flour, crazy foam and pastry, etc. However, it must be a carefully thought-out and well-rehearsed routine. There is nothing worse than slapdash slapstick! A stagecloth is advisable.

The Bedroom Scene

This develops into a farcical romp with lots of leaping in and out of bed, hiding under the bed, a chase, sleepwalking and the ghost of a mad monk! Again, it needs careful thought and must be well rehearsed. The timing of all business, all entrances and exits must be spot on to ensure a fast moving and funny routine.

Other works by Paul Reakes
published by Samuel French Ltd

Pantomimes:

Babes in the Wood
Dick Turpin
King Arthur
Little Jack Horner
Little Miss Muffet
Little Red Riding Hood
Old Mother Hubbard
Robinson Crusoe and the Pirates
Santa in Space
Sinbad the Sailor

Plays:

Bang, You're Dead!
Mantrap

ACT I

Scene 1

Outside Rockbottom's house

UR *is Rockbottom's house with a practical front door. It was once an elegant building but now shows signs of dilapidation. There are other houses. The backcloth and ground row show the rest of the town*

When the CURTAIN *rises, the Chorus, as Tradespeople, Townsfolk and their Children, are discovered. They go straight into the opening song and dance*

Song 1

After the number, a large surly Butcher steps forward or enters L

Butcher All right! All right! That's enough of the pleasantries! Let's get what we came 'ere for! Let's get our money!

He and the other Tradespeople crowd around Rockbottom's house. They bang on the door and yell

Butcher Come out, Rockbottom! We know you're in there!
Tradespeople Rockbottom! Open up! We want our money! We want our money!

The door opens and beautiful young Flora Rockbottom steps out

Flora (*all smiles*) Good-morning.
Butcher I want to see yer father! I've brought him my bill! (*He produces a long bill and waves it under Flora's nose*)

The Tradespeople produce equally long bills of their own and wave them at Flora

Tradespeople (*variously*) And mine! And mine! And mine!
Flora (*nonplussed and not knowing what else to say*) Oh, dear. There does seem to be rather a lot of them.

Butcher Ay! And all *unpaid* too! Go and fetch yer father!
Flora I'm afraid he's not at home at the moment.
1st Tradesperson Huh! A likely story!
Tradespeople (*yelling, waving their bills*) We want our money! (*Etc.*)

They surround Flora, obscuring her from view

Handsome young Robin Reliant walks on L

Robin (*brightly*) Good-morning — I said (*shouting above the din*) *good-morning!!*

The others go silent and step back, revealing Flora

(*Pleasantly surprised*) Oh, hallo Flora. I didn't realize you were part of the scrum.
Flora (*showing some unease*) Hallo, Robin.
Robin (*moving towards the Butcher*) I hope you're not harassing this young lady, Mr Butcher.
Butcher (*growling at him*) Wot if I am! We want our money! (*Rounding on Flora*) Get yer father out!
Flora I've already told you he's not at home.
Butcher Either you get 'im *out* — or we're goin' *in*!
Robin Listen. If Flora says her father is not at home, he's not at home. I suggest you all go away and come back when he is.
Butcher (*advancing on Robin*) Now, look 'ere ...
Robin (*planting his hands on his hips and squaring up to the Butcher*) Didn't you hear me correctly, or have you got sausage meat in your ears! (*Very firmly*) Go — away!
Butcher (*backing down*) A ... All right — we'll go — for now — but we'll be back — we want our money — and we means to get it!

The Butcher stomps out DR. *The other Tradespeople follow him out. The Chorus exit in various directions*

Robin Does your father really owe them all that money?
Flora I'm afraid he does. And a lot of other people besides. Since his button factory went out of business he's been running up debts all over the town. I don't know what we're going to do.
Robin (*putting a comforting arm around her*) I've got two pounds in the building society. He's quite welcome to all of that.
Flora (*smiling in spite of the situation*) Thank you, Robin. It's very kind of you, but I'm afraid it'll take a lot more than that to sort out Father's financial problems.

Robin There is something else I can offer you.
Flora What's that?
Robin My undying love.

Song 2

A romantic duet with romantic lighting

After the number, Robin and Flora embrace

Ruby Rockbottom enters at the back of the auditorium with several carrier bags

Ruby (*calling out to the couple on stage*) Oy! You two! Stop that! Who d'you think you are — (*topical romantic couple*)!
Robin (*to Flora*) That sounds like your sister.
Flora It is. (*Peering out and calling*) Ruby! What are you doing out there?
Ruby (*calling back*) I'll be right with ya, Sis. I'm just minglin' with the masses! (*She makes her way through the audience, waving and chatting to various individuals en route*) Hallo — nice to see ya! Hiya! — I see you've brought Superman out for 'is annual airin'. Hi there — oh, I like the outfit, dear. I didn't know they still made those ... Wake up, Gran. Don't nod off yet ... Oh, you've brought the wife with ya — ooops! No, it *isn't* — sorry! (*She plonks herself into a man's lap*) Ooo! You cheeky thing! Did you see that? 'E pulled me right on to 'is lap. Ooo! Let me go, you insatiable beast! (*At last she clambers on to the stage, hot and bothered*) Whew! I've come over all faint now! (*To Flora*) D'you know what that chap said to me. 'E said 'e wanted to be my toy boy! Flippin' cheek! Toy boy indeed! (*To the audience*) I'll 'ave you know, I'm still in the first *flush* of youth! And no crack about bein' round the bend!
Flora (*indicating the carrier bags*) What have you been doing, Ruby?
Ruby Oh, I've 'ad a wonderful time, Flora. I've been shoppin' in (*local town*). I've bought some smashin' gear! I'll show ya! (*She takes an outrageous green item of clothing from a bag and displays it*) Look at that! Isn't it a humdinger! I'll look like a million dollars in this!
Robin (*amused*) Yes — all green and crinkly.

Ignoring him Ruby stuffs the item away and produces a very small, skimpy red bra. Robin roars with laughter

(*To the audience*) She'll never get into that, will she?
Ruby (*to the audience*) Oh, yes, I will!

"Oh no, you won't/oh, yes, I will" routine follows. In a huff, Ruby stuffs the bra away and takes out another shocking dress

(*Displaying it*) How about this little bobby dazzler! I'll certainly turn the men's heads when I wear this.

Robin Yes — and their stomachs!

Ruby (*to Robin, stuffing the dress into a bag*) You know your trouble, don't ya! You've got no idea about up-to-date fashion. Just look at ya! Stood standin' there in Madonna's cast-offs! (*Or something appropriate to Robin's costume*)

Flora Ruby, where did you get the money to pay for all this?

Ruby *Money*! Oh, I never carry money, our sis, y' know that! I'm like the Queen. I put it on Daddy's account.

Flora (*unable to believe her ears*) You did *what*? Oh, Ruby, how could you be so stupid. Father won't be able to pay for it. You know he's up to his ears in debt. You're going to have to take them all back to the shops.

Ruby (*whining*) But I can't do that! I'll look a proper twerp. What'll I say?

Robin Tell them you've decided to join a nudist camp!

Flora (*kindly, but firm*) Take them all back, Ruby — now.

Ruby (*pouting*) Oh … All right!

Robin and Flora exit R

Sulkily, Ruby dumps the bags to one side and turns to the audience with a sigh

Tch! Innit rotten bein' poor! (*She gives a big "Ahh!" and encourages the audience to follow suit*) Once upon a time we Rockbottoms were the richest family in town. Mohammed Al Fayed used to deliver our groceries personally! Now we can't even afford a tin of tuna from Tesco's! (*Dramatically*) Oh, what's to become of me! I'm used to livin' in luxury — an' I don't want to move! (*Brightening*) There's only one hope for it. I must marry a rich man to look after me. Any offers? What about you, young man? You look like you've got a nice big lump sum hidden away. No? Well, please yerself! It shouldn't be too difficult to find someone. After all — (*she preens herself*) I'm young — I'm beautiful — and *I'm desperate*!

Song 3

A comedy song and dance

Oh, well! While I'm waitin' for (*well-known wealthy man*) to come along I suppose I'd better take these back to the shops. (*She picks up the bags, moves to the front of stage, then stops*) No. I don't think I'll go *that* way again. (*Pointing to man whose lap she sat on*) 'E's 'ad enough excitement for one day! (*Waving, she moves to exit* R). Ta ta! See you later!

Ruby exits

Fetch and Carrie enter L, *pushing a large laundry basket on wheels in which Rockbottom is concealed. They halt* C, *and sit on the basket, getting their breath back. Fetch becomes aware of the audience*

Fetch (*nudging Carrie*) Here! We've got company. (*Pointing to the audience*) Look!
Carrie (*looking*) Cor! So we have!

They get up and move forward

Carrie Who are they? D' you think they're leftovers from (*local event*)?
Fetch I don't think so. Shall we fraternize with them?
Carrie No — let's try talkin' to them first.
Fetch
Carrie } (*together*) Hallo!

The audience call back

Fetch Well, at least they're alive.
Carrie I'm not too sure about that one over there.
Fetch I suppose we'd better introduce ourselves. We're servants to the Rockbottom family. I'm Fetch.
Carrie And I'm Carrie.
Fetch Our main job at the moment is keeping old Rockbottom hidden from his creditors. It isn't easy, and ... (*Struck by a sudden thought*) Oh, no! I've just thought! He's still in there!

They rush back to the basket and Fetch taps on the lid

Mr Rockbottom! Are you all right?

Mumbles from inside the basket

Carrie We'd better get him out before he supplicates!
Fetch (*tapping on the lid*) Mr Rockbottom!

Mumbles from the basket

It's all right. There's no-one about. We're going to let you out.

They lift the lid

The head of Rockbottom emerges from the basket. It has a large bra draped over it

Rockbottom Ee! By 'eck! It's 'ot in 'ere! Are tha sure there's none o' them creditors about?
Fetch There's no-one here but us.
Rockbottom That's all reight then! 'Elp me out o' this contraption.

They haul him out of the basket. In the process the bra slips over his eyes

Ee up! Who put t' lights out?!
Fetch It's all right. Your ear muffs have slipped. (*He removes the bra and drops it into the basket*)
Rockbottom (*sniffing with disgust*) Phew! There's a reight 'orrible pong around 'ere! (*He sniffs*) By 'eck! Where's it comin' from?!

Fetch extracts a large sock from down the back of Rockbottom's collar. In disgust, he throws it to Carrie, who throws it to Rockbottom, who throws it to Fetch. They throw the sock to each other, and even threaten to throw it out into the audience. It gets thrown off stage, only to be thrown back again. Eventually, it gets thrown into the basket, and all three sit on the lid

(*Despondently*) Ee! What a come down. Me, Eli Rockbottom, once the biggest button maker in the business, reduced to 'idin' from me creditors in a lousy laundry basket!
Fetch Cheer up, sir. Something is bound to turn up.
Carrie Yes. You know the old sayin': every silver cloud has a torn lining!

Song 4

A cheer-up song and dance for Fetch and Carrie. Eventually, Rockbottom forgets his troubles and joins in

After the number, the angry voices of the Butcher and Tradespeople are heard

Butcher } (*together, off* R) { Come on, let's get our money!
Tradespeople } { We want our money! (*Etc.*)
Rockbottom (*panicking*) Ee up! It's me creditors!!
Fetch Quick! Back in the basket!
Rockbottom Oh, no! Not that smelly sock again!

They bundle him into the basket and shut the lid. They assume a nonchalant air

The Butcher and Tradespeople enter R. *The Chorus enter from various directions*

Butcher Right! Where is he?
Fetch
Carrie } (*together*) Who?
Butcher (*bellowing at them*) Rockbottom!!

The force of his bellow knocks them back L

Fetch Oh, you want Mr Rockbottom … No, we haven't seen him … (*To Carrie*) have we?
Carrie Not a bit of him.
Butcher (*to the others*) Perhaps he sneaked back into the house! Come on!

The Butcher and the Tradespeople turn towards the house. A loud sneeze comes from the basket, making the lid jump. The Butcher and the others stop and turn around. Fetch pretends to be wiping his nose

Fetch Sorry — hay fever.

They turn back to the house. Another loud sneeze rattles the basket. The Butcher and his gang stop and turn around again

Carrie (*desperately*) Saturday Night Fever? (*She does a few dance steps*)

With great suspicion the Butcher marches up to the basket, followed by the others

Fetch and Carrie, sensing danger, creep away L *and exit*

The Butcher taps on the lid of the basket

Rockbottom (*calling from inside*) 'Ave they gone?
Butcher (*roaring*) No, they haven't!!

He throws back the lid and hauls Rockbottom up by his collar. The others gather behind the basket

Rockbottom (*lamely*) Mornin' … mornin' … turned out nice again …

Butcher We've come for our money, Rockbottom! Pay up — or else!

He shakes Rockbottom by the collar, as the others wave their bills

Tradespeople Give us our money! We want our money! (*Etc.*)
Fetch
Carrie } (*together, off* L, *yelling above the din*) *Fire!! Fire!! Fire!!*

Fetch and Carrie rush on to great excitement, yelling "Fire!" at the top of their voices

The Tradespeople quickly lose interest in Rockbottom

Fetch Fire! The whole of Market Street is going up in flames!
Carrie You'd better hurry up if you want to save your shops! *Fire!! Fire!!*

In a panic, the Butcher and the Tradespeople rush out L, *followed by the Chorus*

Rockbottom By gum! Market Street on fire! What a catastrophe!
Fetch It will be when they find out we were just kiddin'! Quick! Get into the house and bolt the door!

Rockbottom jumps out of the basket and rushes into the house, slamming the door behind him. Fetch and Carrie exit DR *with the basket*

Bluebeard enters UL. *He sweeps on grandly as if expecting a welcoming committee. He is followed by Lurkin, his grotesque, hunchbacked servant*

Bluebeard (*disappointed and angry*) Bah! There is no-one here to welcome me! The place is deserted! It's empty! Just like the space between your ears, Lurkin! (*Venting his anger, he cuffs Lurkin*)
Lurkin (*always grateful*) Thank you, master.

Bluebeard moves down C, *and Lurkin scuttles to his side*

Lurkin P'raps they ain't 'eard of your arrival yet, master.
Bluebeard (*pompously*) How could they not! My magnificence precedes me! They must know that *I* have taken up residence near their miserable, misbegotten mole heap of a town! (*He gets carried away in a reverie of self-glorification*) I, Great Baron Bluebeard! Bluebeard, the magnificant! Bluebeard, the stupendous! Bluebeard, the envy of all men and the desire of all women!

Lurkin (*to the audience*) An' 'e's very modest wiv it!

Bluebeard (*spinning round*) Who are you talking to, worm?

Lurkin (*cringing and pointing to the audience*) Them, master.

Bluebeard (*to the audience*) So! There is a reception committee after all! (*Scanning the audience and sneering*) Pah! What a mouldy looking mob of misfits! You're not fit to lick my boots! You're not fit to gaze upon my wondrous appendage!

Lurkin (*to the audience*) 'E means 'is face fungus!

Bluebeard If *these* pathetic specimens are anything to go by, this town is solely inhabited by penniless riff-raff. I shall not find what I most desire in this nauseating neck of the woods! I should never have come here in the first place. Tomorrow I will go down to (*local estate agents*) and put the castle on the market.

Lurkin But, master, you ain't give it a chance. (*Darkly*) Who knows—there might be somethin' 'ere worth sniffin' out.

Bluebeard (*grabbing him in rage*) Listen, you snivelling snail! If there was something worth sniffing, I'd have sniffed it! All I'm sniffing at the moment is *you*! (*He cuffs Lurkin and pushes him away*)

Ruby enters UL. *She stops and stands listening*

Lurkin Thank you, master. P'raps you ought to take a little break. It ain't as if you can't afford to. You are the richest man in the world.

Ruby's ears prick up on hearing this

Bluebeard True! But I want more! *More*! (*Grabbing Lurkin; insanely*) *D'you hear me! More! More! More!*

Lurkin has to calm him down

Ruby (*to the audience*) The richest man in the world, eh! It looks like Mr Right has arrived, girls! (*She gives herself a quick preen, then pushes in between Bluebeard and Lurkin*) Hallo! (*She flutters her eyelashes at Bluebeard and tries to look demure*) I'm Ruby Rockbottom. I don't believe I've 'ad the pleasure.

Bluebeard (*aside*) And I'm not surprised! (*To her*) I am — Baron Bluebeard! (*He strikes a pose and flicks his beard*)

Ruby 'Ere! You ought to sue them, y' know.

Bluebeard Who?

Ruby The ones who did that to yer soup strainer! That would never 'ave 'appened at (*local hairdressers*)!

Bluebeard (*stroking his beard*) I prefer it this colour. It marches my eyes.

Ruby You should 'ave 'ad it done in *red* then! (*She laughs and gives him a friendly push*)

Bluebeard is stone-faced. Lurkin goes into convulsions of laughter. The other two stare at him and his laughter dissolves into an embarrassed cough

Ruby (*to Bluebeard*) Aren't you gonna introduce me to your pet monkey?
Bluebeard (*airily*) He is one of my many minions.
Lurkin (*sidling up to Ruby with a grotesque leer*) I'm Lurkin.
Ruby Yes … well … don't do it near me!
Lurkin I 'ad a *hunch* you were gonna say that!
Bluebeard (*to Ruby*) Tell me, what is your position?
Ruby Oh! You cheeky thing, you! (*She gives him a playful push*)
Bluebeard (*recovering*) You misunderstand me, Mrs — er ——
Ruby Oh, I'm not a *Mrs*! Oh, no! I'm a miss! I'm single! I'm free! (*Sidling up to him in a deep, sexy voice*) I'm up for grabs!
Bluebeard (*taking a step back*) I see. Are your people solvent?
Ruby No, C of E.
Bluebeard I mean — do they have money?
Ruby (*gushing*) What us? Oh, yes! Rollin' in it! We're part of the effluent society! Filthy rich, we are! Positively filthy!

Bluebeard and Lurkin exchange glances. Bluebeard now puts on his oily charm

Bluebeard I see. And you say you are unattached, Miss Stonebottom?
Ruby *Rock*bottom! Oh, yes! I'm unattached. I'm completely unhinged, in fact!
Bluebeard Then — (*he takes her hand*) allow me. (*He kisses her hand*)
Ruby (*squirming with delight*) Ooo! That tickles!
Bluebeard It just so happens I am looking for a spouse.
Ruby Oh, they're buildin' some new ones at (*local place*).
Bluebeard (*with momentary annoyance*) I said *spouse* not house! (*Oily charm again*) I wish to take a wife. Someone, perhaps — (*taking her hands*) like you, Miss Flintbottom.
Ruby *Rock*bottom! (*Acting coyly*) Oh, sir! Are you asking me to be your awful wedded wife?
Bluebeard (*going down on one knee*) I am!
Ruby (*O.T.T.*) Oh, this is so sudden! What is a poor girl to do!
Lurkin (*sidling up to her*) Say yes. It's the last chance *you'll* get! (*He chortles*)

Ruby gives him a hefty push and turns back to Bluebeard

Ruby Yes! Oh, yes! I will be thine! (*She clamps his head in a bear hug, then hauls him to his feet. Very businesslike*) Come on! Let's get hitched!
Bluebeard There is something to be settled first — my love. The little matter of your dowry. (*He rubs his hands*)
Ruby My *what*-ary?!
Bluebeard As you must know, it is customary for a father to pay a handsome sum of money to the man who is willing to take a daughter off his hands. Take me to your father so that I may discuss the matter with him.
Ruby (*in a turmoil*) Well ... I — I ...
Bluebeard Not a problem, is there? You told me your family had money.
Lurkin Filthy rich, you said!
Ruby (*nervously*) Well ... er ... not so much filthy rich — just a bit grubby.
Bluebeard I hope you're not wasting my time! Lurkin! Show her how we deal with time-wasters!
Lurkin (*with devilish glee*) Yes, master!

He advances to Ruby, menacingly. Yelling, she runs to the house, finds the door locked and bangs on it

Ruby (*yelling*) 'Elp!! Daddy!! Let me in!! 'Elp!!

The door is opened and Rockbottom sticks his head out

Rockbottom Ruby, lass! What's to do?
Ruby (*pulling him outside*) Oh, Daddy! Save me! (*She hides behind Rockbottom*)
Bluebeard I take it you are the father of this — *this*.
Rockbottom Ay! Eli Rockbottom's t' name. What's tha want?
Bluebeard I wish to marry your daughter.
Rockbottom (*dumbfounded*) What *'er*?! Our Ruby ?! By 'eck! Well, take 'er, lad, wi' my blessin'. (*He pushes Ruby towards Bluebeard*)
Bluebeard Not until we have discussed the marriage settlement.
Rockbottom (*flabbergasted*) Y' mean you want *me* to pay *you*!
Bluebeard Certainly!

Rockbottom bursts out laughing

Rockbottom Ha! Ha! Ha! By gum! That's a good un! I don't know what's she's been tellin' thee, but I'm flat broke! I 'aven't got a bean! Ha! Ha! Ha!
Bluebeard (*to Ruby, enraged*) *You!!!*

Ruby beats a hasty exit into the house

Rockbottom is helpless with laughter. Bluebeard vents his anger on Lurkin and cuffs him

Lurkin Thank you, master.

Bluebeard sweeps towards the exit, DL. *He almost bumps into Flora*

Flora enters DL, *followed by Robin*

Flora Oh, excuse me.
Bluebeard (*obviously liking the look of her and turning on the oily charm*) No — pray excuse me.

He steps back and bows, allowing Flora to pass in front of him. She and Robin cross to Rockbottom, who is leaning against the house, holding his side

Flora Father! What's the matter?
Rockbottom Oh, Flora, m' dear. Ee, I think I've done misen a mischief wi' all that laughin'. Yon chap wi' the blue rinse — 'e wants to marry tha sister Ruby! An' if that weren't funny enough, 'e wants *me* to pay 'er dowry! (*He laughs and holds his side*)
Bluebeard (*moving over slightly*) Am I to understand that this charming young lady is another daughter of yours?
Rockbottom Ay! Me youngest. Our Flora.
Bluebeard (*to Flora, oozing oily charm*) I am greatly honoured to make your acquaintance, Miss Flora. I am — Baron Bluebeard! (*He strikes a pose and flicks his beard*)
Flora I am pleased to meet you, Baron. May I introduce Mr Robin Reliant.
Robin (*presenting his hand to Bluebeard*) How do you do.

Bluebeard looks Robin up and down, then sneers

Bluebeard I never shake hands with commoners. (*He turns his back on the snubbed Robin*) Rockbottom, there is a matter I wish to discuss with you — in private.
Rockbottom Certainly, Baron. But if it's about payin' for our Ruby, I ——
Bluebeard This is an entirely different matter. Something to *your* advantage,
Rockbottom (*interested*) Oh!

A commotion is heard, and some of the Tradespeople and Chorus enter L

1st Tradesperson There's Rockbottom!
Rockbottom Oh, no! (*He dashes to the exit* DR)

The Butcher and the rest of the Tradespeople and Chorus enter DR

Rockbottom is forced back to C. *The Tradespeople gather around him, waving their bills*

Tradespeople (*yelling*) Give us our money! We want our money! Pay up! (*Etc.*)
Bluebeard (*bellowing above the din*) *Silence!!*

They all go silent and look at him

What is the meaning of this disturbance?
Butcher Well, if it's any of *your* business, we want our money! The money Rockbottom owes us! (*Showing the bill*) Look!

The others wave their bills

Bluebeard (*glancing at the bill*) Pah! A mere trifle! Lurkin!
Lurkin (*scuttling to his side*) Yes, master?
Bluebeard (*producing a bulging money bag*) Pay these persons what Mr Rockbottom owes them.

Gasps and exclamations from all the Tradespeople. Lurkin takes the bag and goes US. *The Butcher and the others gather around him to be paid*

Rockbottom (*overwhelmed*) T-Thank you, Baron ... I don't know what to say ... I'll not be able to repay tha, tha knows.
Bluebeard (*darkly*) That remains to be seen. Now can we discuss that matter I mentioned.
Rockbottom (*grovelling*) Certainly, Baron. This way ... this way.

He goes up to the house and holds the door open. Bluebeard is about to follow, then observes Flora and Robin together, holding hands

Bluebeard I should like Miss Flora to join us.
Rockbottom Of course, Baron. Flora! (*He indicates for her to join them*)

Flora and Robin start towards the house, still hand in hand

Bluebeard On her own!

The couple hesitate

Rockbottom You 'eard the baron, Flora!

The couple part

Flora goes into the house. Bluebeard gives Robin a disdainful look and goes in after her. Rockbottom follows and closes the door behind him

Robin goes up and stares at the closed door

Having distributed the money, Lurkin pushes past Robin and goes into the house

The Butcher and the Tradespeople come forward, overjoyed at being paid at last

Robin (*turning away from the door and confronting them*) I don't know how you could take that man's money. He makes my flesh creep.
Butcher Who cares what *you* think! He paid Rockbottom's bills, that's all *we* care about!

The others agree

Robin (*looking towards the house with suspicion*) Yes — why did he do that? He doesn't strike me as being the generous sort. And why did he want Flora to join them? I think he's up to something. And I'm going to find out what it is!

Robin marches out DR

Butcher (*scoffing*) You do that! (*To the others*) We've got our money, and that's all that matters to us!
Tradespeople Ay!

The Tradespeople and Chorus go into a short reprise of Song 1

Song 4a (Reprise of Song 1)

After the number, the Lights fade to Black-out. Music covers the scene change

Scene 2

A room in Rockbottom's house

Tabs, or a frontcloth showing a shabby room in a house that has seen better days

Fetch creeps on DL. *He tiptoes across to* DR, *and crouches as if listening at a door. Carrie creeps on* DL, *tiptoes across to Fetch and also listens. Ruby enters* DL. *She gives them a puzzled look, then tiptoes across to Carrie and listens. All three crouch in silence for a while*

Ruby (*loudly*) What are you ——?
Fetch (*to Carrie*) Shhh!!
Carrie (*to Ruby*) Shhh!!
Ruby (*to thin air* L) Shhhhh!!!

They react to each other and move downstage

What are you doin'?
Fetch That Baron Bluebeard's in there with your father. We were trying to hear what he's saying.
Ruby It's very rude to listen at key 'oles! — What *is* 'e sayin'?
Fetch Whatever it is, I bet it's something shifty. From what I've seen of Bluebeard, I wouldn't trust him an inch!
Carrie Nor me. 'E makes (*current media baddies*) look like Sooty and Sweep!
Ruby Mm, you're right. There is something a bit fishy about him. Any man who changes 'is mind about wantin' to marry me, can't be right in the 'ead, can 'e?

They say nothing and look away

All right! Don't take a vote on it!
Fetch Let's try listening again.
Ruby Right! But we'd better watch out for Bluebeard's henchman — or hunchman — or what ever 'e is! Y' know, old — (*she does an impression of Lurkin*). 'E's 'angin' around the house somewhere.
Carrie (*indicating the audience*) Our mates 'll warn us if 'e shows 'is ugly mug. (*To the audience*) Won't you, folks?
Audience Yes.

They give the audience the thumbs-up sign, then go to listen at the unseen door DR

Unseen by them, Lurkin enters from DL, *and goes over so he's behind them*

The audience will be shouting warnings

Fetch
Ruby
Carrie (*together to the audience*) Is it him?!

Audience Yes.
Fetch
Ruby (*together to the audience*) Where is he?!
Carrie

"He's behind you!" routine. Comic business with the three turning and Lurkin always keeping behind them. This is repeated a couple of times until they see him. Fetch, Ruby and Carrie yell, and run towards the exit DL. *Lurkin grabs Ruby before she can escape*

Fetch and Carrie exit

Lurkin There's no need for *you* to go. (*Pulling her closer*) You stay an' talk to me.
Ruby I — I'd love to, but I've left somethin' on the stove!

She pulls free and makes for the exit DL, *but Lurkin gets there first*

Oh! Isn't there a mad scientist somewhere you should be assistin'?
Lurkin You're confusin' me with my cousin Ygor. 'E works for Dr Frankenstein. They're in the body buildin' business. 'E'd love to meet you! Ygor's always on the look out for spare parts! 'E'd love your eyes — your nose — your lips — your chin — your ——
Ruby That's enough of the shoppin' list! Listen, Humpty Dumpty, all these bits are mine, an' they're gonna stay mine!

Ruby pushes him away and runs out DL

Bluebeard enters DR, *followed by Rockbottom, who is looking a bit uneasy*

Bluebeard So! Are we agreed?
Rockbottom It's a very generous offer, Baron, but I'll naturally have to talk t' lass first. I can't agree on nowt wi'out askin' 'er first. It's only fair.
Bluebeard (*irritably*) Oh, very well! Lurkin! Find Miss Flora and bring her here.
Lurkin Yes, master.

Lurkin scuttles out DL

Bluebeard I hope she will not prove difficult, Rockbottom.
Rockbottom You never can tell wi' lasses. She's very keen on that young Robin Reliant …

Bluebeard Pah! That penniless poltroon! What kind of husband would he make! I am prepared to pay you *one thousand gold pieces* for Flora's hand in marriage.
Rockbottom I know! (*Ecstatically*) Ee! I could pay off all me debts wi' that kind o' brass! I could even start t' button factory up again!
Bluebeard Then it is up to you to persuade Flora to say yes.
Rockbottom (*crashing down to earth*) Ay!

Flora enters DL, *followed by Lurkin*

Flora (*crossing to Rockbottom*) Yes, Father?
Rockbottom (*uneasy*) Flora, m' dear ... I've got some champion news for thee ... Baron Bluebeard has — has asked for your 'and in marriage.
Flora (*aghast*) *What*!
Bluebeard (*to her, with oily charm*) I trust you will accept my proposal.
Flora (*ignoring him and turning to Rockbottom*) Father, have you taken leave of your senses! You expect me to marry a complete stranger?
Rockbottom (*coaxingly*) 'E's offerin' a thousand gold pieces. It'll save me from ruin!
Flora And what about *me*? Don't *my* feelings matter? No! I refuse to be sold off like a piece of furniture! (*To Bluebeard*) No, Baron, I do not accept your proposal! (*She moves away and folds her arms in defiance*)
Rockbottom (*going back to Bluebeard and shrugging*) Well, I tried. 'Appen you'll reconsider our Ruby. You'd be getting' a lot more fer yer money.

Bluebeard gives him a frightful glare

I must admit, Baron, the girl's reight. I can't expect 'er to marry a stranger — not even for a thousand gold pieces.
Bluebeard (*musing*) Mm — you are right, Rockbottom. Of course we are strangers. But I intend to rectify that. I invite you and your daughters to spend a few days at my castle. There, we can all become better acquainted. If, after that time, Flora still finds me unacceptable as a husband we will forget the whole matter. (*Slight pause*) Also, the one thousand gold pieces will be yours, regardless of the outcome.
Rockbottom (*enthused*) By 'eck! That sounds fair! (*Scuttling to Flora*) what d' you say, Flora?
Flora (*warily*) Well, I ...
Rockbottom (*taking her aside and whispering*) Listen. All we've got to do is go to 'is castle for a couple o' days. Tha tells 'im to sling 'is 'ook, an' we come 'ome wi' all that brass! Oh, say tha'll do it fer yer old dad!
Flora (*sighing*) Oh, very well. For your sake.
Rockbottom (*delighted and kissing her*) Ee! Champion! (*To Bluebeard*) She's agreed to it!

Bluebeard Excellent!
Rockbottom When do tha want us at t' castle?
Bluebeard There's no time like the present. We shall leave as soon as you've made arrangements for the journey.
Rockbottom Come on, lass! Let's tell Ruby an' start packin'!

Rockbottom hustles Flora out DR

As soon as they are out of sight, Bluebeard rubs his hands and bursts into laughter. Puzzled, Lurkin scuttles to his side

Lurkin Master, are you feelin' all right? It ain't like you to be *partin'* wi' money!
Bluebeard Fear not, my trusty troll. Your master has not lost his reason. The money is a lure to get them into the castle. Once there, we will dispose of Rockbottom and that revolting Ruby!
Lurkin (*with devilish glee*) Oh, master! I can't wait! And the girl?
Bluebeard She has genuinely taken my fancy, and will amuse me for as long as I see fit. Once I have grown tired of her she will go the same way as all the others.
Lurkin (*adoringly*) Oh, master! It's an honour to bask in your beastliness.

They exit DL, *sneering and snarling at the audience*

Fetch and Carrie enter DR, *as Robin hurries on* DL

Robin Hey! You two! What's going on?
Fetch Bluebeard's taking the Rockbottoms to his castle.
Carrie Family only! We're circus to requirements.
Robin (*suspiciously*) I don't like the sound of that.
Carrie No, I don't think it's the right word!
Robin Bluebeard is up to no good, I'm convinced of it.
Fetch That's just what I think. What can we do?
Robin There's only one thing we *can* do! We'll have to follow them to the castle and make sure nothing happens.
Carrie (*very apprehensive*) That sounds a bit dangerous! Couldn't we just wait 'ere and see if anything' 'appens to 'em on *Crimewatch*?

Fetch gives Carrie a push

Robin (*stepping forward, valiantly*) I would go through fire and water to protect Flora. The girl I love! (*He slaps his thigh*)
Fetch Ay! (*He slaps his thigh*)

Carrie Ay! (*She slaps her thigh*) Cor! That 'urts!
Robin Come on!

Robin runs out DL

Fetch goes to follow, then sees Carrie hanging back

Fetch Well, come on!
Carrie I'll give it a miss. I don't feel well! I've got a bone in my leg … (*limping*) look! I *am* the weakest link — goodbye! (*She makes to go*)

Fetch grabs her arm and drags her out DL

The Lights fade to Black-out. Music to cover the scene change

Scene 3

A wood near Bluebeard's castle

Tree wings and a foliage ground row. The backcloth shows more trees and a sinister looking castle on a hill in the distance

The Lights come up on the Chorus, as Peasants and their Children. The adults sing and clap as the Dancers and the Children perform a merry country dance

Song 5

After the number, the adults cheer and applaud the Dancers and Children

During this, Bluebeard enters R, *followed by Lurkin, Flora and Rockbottom. He wears a travelling cape and hat. She, a hooded cloak*

Bluebeard (*to the Chorus*) Silence! What is the meaning of this nauseating nonsense?
Peasant Beggin' yer pardon, zur. We always come into this wood to relax a'ter a 'ard day's work in the fields.
Bluebeard Not anymore! I am Baron Bluebeard! The new owner of yonder castle and its surrounding lands. That includes this wood. You are trespassing! Get out, and never set foot here again!

Noisy protests from the Peasants

Bluebeard Lurkin! See them off!
Lurkin Yes, master!

Lurkin draws an evil-looking dagger and advances on the Peasants, menacingly

The Peasants shrink back and run out L

Flora (*to Bluebeard*) Was that really necessary? They were doing no harm.
Bluebeard They were trespassing on *my* property! Come, let us continue on our journey.
Flora We can't. My sister hasn't caught up with us yet.
Rockbottom (*calling to off* R) Come on, Ruby! You're 'oldin' us up, lass!

Ruby enters R. *She is comically dressed for travelling, and staggers under the weight of several suitcases, hat boxes and other luggage parapherna-lia, including a rolled umbrella*

Ruby I don't know why *I've* got to carry this lot! I'm not Charlie Dimmock, y'know!
Lurkin (*aside*) She can say that again! More like Tommy Walsh! (*He cackles*)
Ruby (*huffily*) I'm glad you think it's so funny! (*To the audience, groaning*) Oow! I'm sure I've strained summit! I've probably pulled a liniment! (*To someone*) But nobody cares, do they, dear? Nobody cares! (*Byplay with the audience*)
Bluebeard (*impatiently*) Enough of this dallying! Let us be on our way!
Ruby 'Ang on! 'Ang on! I need a rest! Can't you see I'm carryin' all this weight? Don't answer that! (*To the audience*) You think I deserve a rest, don't you, folks?
Audience Yes!
Bluebeard (*to the audience*) Oh, no, she doesn't!

A routine with the audience follows. Ruby piles up the suitcases and sits on them

Ruby There! (*To Bluebeard*) I'm takin' a rest whether you like it or not! (*She folds her arms*)
Bluebeard Lurkin! Move her!

Lurkin looks at Ruby

Lurkin (*shaking his head*) Not without a forklift, master.

Bluebeard (*disgruntled*) Oh, very well! You can rest for five minutes! (*Turning to Flora, with oily charm*) It will give me an opportunity of showing you the rest of the wood. (*Offering her his arm*) Allow me.

Flora ignores his offer and walks out L

Bluebeard reacts, then goes to follow her

Rockbottom (*moving over*) Can I come too?
Bluebeard If you must!

Bluebeard exits L, *followed by Rockbottom*

Lurkin lingers, leering across at Ruby. She sees him and does a double-take

Lurkin (*moving a bit closer*) Shall I stay an' keep you company?
Ruby No thanks! Why don't you go and polish yer gargoyles!

Lurkin shambles off L

(*To the audience*) I'm gonna 'ave forty winks. If 'e tries to sneak up on me, give us a shout, will ya?

Audience Yes!

She thanks them, then yawns and dozes off to sleep

Lurkin creeps on from L

The audience shout. Ruby wakes up

Lurkin scuttles off L

Ruby (*looking about, muttering*) False alarm. (*She goes back to sleep*)

Lurkin creeps on again

The audience shout but Ruby doesn't wake up. He moves right up close to her. She opens one eye and sees him looming over her. Yelling, she falls backwards off the cases, her legs in the air. Lurkin eagerly grabs her ankles

(*Kicking him away*) *Get off!! Get off!!* (*She scrabbles to her feet and grabs the umbrella*)

Lurkin Oo! You're lovely when you're angry!
Ruby (*charging at him with the umbrella*) *Gerr out of it!!*

Lurkin scuttles out L

(*Sitting on the cases*) Just let 'im try that again! I'll give 'im a lump on 'is 'ump! (*She yawns*) Don't forget to warn me, kids. (*She goes to sleep*)

Fetch and Carrie creep on UR

They see Ruby, and tiptoe down to her. Fetch taps her gently on the shoulder. She wakes with a start, and bashes them with her umbrella

Fetch (*as they are being hit*) Oy! Oy!
Ruby (*recognizing them*) Oh, it's you two!

Robin runs on from UR, *and comes straight down to Ruby*

Robin (*very concerned*) Where's Flora? What's he done with her? What's happened? Where is she?
Ruby (*huffily*) Huh! And a hallo to you an' all!
Robin I'm sorry, Ruby, but I'm very concerned about Flora's safety. Where is she?
Ruby The Baron's showin' 'er and Daddy the wood, while I take a semester — (*to the audience*) that's French for 'avin a kip. (*To Robin*) What's goin' on? What are you three doin' 'ere?
Robin We decided to follow you. We don't trust Bluebeard an inch.
Fetch We think he's up to jiggery-pokery.
Carrie Yeah! An' dullskuggery!
Robin I can't understand why your father accepted his invitation in the first place.
Ruby I can! Brass! Old Bluebag's gonna give Daddy a thousand gold pieces!

Reaction from the others

Robin Why?
Ruby As a sweetener. 'E wants to marry Flora.
Robin (*aghast*) *What*?!
Ruby I know! I can't understand it either. Specially when 'e could 'ave 'ad *me*! But don't worry, lover boy, she's not goin' to. As soon as we've got the money we're goin' 'ome!
Robin I don't trust Bluebeard. Why don't you persuade your father and Flora to return home now before it's too late.

Ruby And say goodbye to all that money! Daddy'll never do that. 'E'd rather kiss (*unattractive celebrity*) ! You know 'e's desperate for cash.
Robin Yes. Well, we'll just have to keep on following you. As soon as you get to the castle you'll have to find a way of getting us inside. We'll hide and keep watch. If Bluebeard tries anything we'll be on hand to come to the rescue. (*To Fetch and Carrie*) Won't we?
Fetch (*stoutly*) I'm right with you!
Carrie I'm — sure I left a tap runnin'! ...

Carrie makes a dash for the exit, but Fetch pulls her back

Ruby (*looking off* L) Look out! 'E's comin' back!

Robin, Fetch and Carrie run out R

Ruby sits on the cases

Bluebeard enters, followed by Flora, Rockbottom and Lurkin

Bluebeard It's time to be moving on. I want to reach the castle before nightfall.
Ruby Afraid of missin' (*soap opera*), I suppose! (*She stands up and groans*) Oh, can't someone 'elp me carry this lot?
Bluebeard Lurkin! Assist her with the luggage. (*To the others*) Come!

Bluebeard exits L, *followed by Flora and Rockbottom. Lurkin goes over, selects the smallest item of luggage and exits* L

Ruby Don't strain yerself, will ya! (*Grumbling to herself, she gathers up the luggage and staggers to the exit* L. *She stops, calling to off* R) Oy! Calling international rescue!

The heads of Robin, Fetch and Carrie appear R

It's time to do yer stuff!

Ruby exits L

Robin creeps on R *and moves* C, *followed by Fetch and Carrie. Robin signals for them to follow and makes a stealthy exit* L. *Fetch is close behind him, but Carrie is tiptoeing away in the opposite direction. Fetch grabs her and drags her out* L

A Peasant creeps on upstage, looks about, then beckons. The other Peasants enter and perform a short reprise of Song 5

Song 5a (Reprise of Song 5)

The Lights fade to Black-out. Music to cover the scene change

Scene 4

A passage in Bluebeard's castle

Tabs, or a frontcloth showing dark, slimy walls hung with grim-looking weapons and armour, etc.

The Lights come up to give a gloomy effect

Marie, a pretty young French kitchen-maid, creeps on DR. *She pauses to look about, then creeps towards the exit* DL

The dark and sinister figure of Mrs Shivers enters DR, *and glides to* C. *She always moves with a strange, gliding motion that gives her the appearance of floating above the ground*

Sensing her eerie presence, Marie stops and turns. Mrs Shivers says nothing, but points a bony finger in the direction of the DR *exit. Timidly, Marie scuttles out* DR

Shivers glides to the back and remains motionless in the shadows

Bluebeard enters DR, *followed by Rockbottom, Flora and Lurkin*

Bluebeard (*grandly*) Welcome! Welcome to Castle Bluebeard! (*He moves* L)

Rockbottom and Flora look at their dark and gloomy surroundings

Ruby staggers on DR, *still burdened with the luggage*

Ruby (*huffing and puffing*) Phew! Cor! I shall 'ave arms like a flippin' orang-utan at this rate! (*She moves* C, *taking in her surroundings*). Crikey! Is this *it*?! Talk about doom an' gloom! (*To Bluebeard*) 'Ere! You wanna get (Changing Rooms *presenter*) in! (*To Rockbottom*) It's 'ardly the (*local posh hotel*), is it? More like the (*local pub*) at chuckin' out time!

Bluebeard (*indignantly*) This is only a back passage!
Ruby (*aside to Rockbottom*) There's no answer to that!

During this aside, Shivers glides down and stands beside Ruby. Ruby turns away from Rockbottom and is confronted by Shivers. She yells and leaps back

Yaaaah!! It's Dracula's Granny!!
Bluebeard This is my housekeeper — Mrs Shivers.
Ruby
Flora
Rockbottom } (*together to Shivers, with some apprehension*) How d'you do.

Shivers just bows her head slightly

Bluebeard This is Mr Rockbottom and his two daughters. They will be spending a few days at the castle.

Again, Shivers just bows her head

Ruby (*aside to Rockbottom*) Right little chatterbox, isn't she! (*To Shivers*) I'm sure I've seen you somewhere before. Aren't you a member of (*local WI*)? Didn't I see you on the pickle stall?
Shivers (*in a voice to match her sinister appearance*) I am afraid you are mistaken, miss. I never leave the castle — during daylight hours.

Ruby reacts

Bluebeard Shivers will now show you to your rooms. We shall meet again at dinner.
Ruby Oh, great! Dinner! I could do with a bite! (*To Shivers*) Forget I said that!
Shivers Please walk this way.

Shivers glides out DL. *The Rockbottoms watch her strange departure, then Rockbottom and Flora exit* DL

Ruby goes to follow, but pauses to speak to someone in the front row of the audience

Ruby You'd better call Buffy! I think we're gonna need 'er!

She exits warily DL

Lurkin (*drawing his dagger with evil relish*) Shall I go an' kill 'em now, master?

Bluebeard Patience, you putrid parasite! We shall dispose of them very soon — with *this*! (*He produces a small poison bottle*) One drop of this poison means *instant death*! Ha! Ha! Ha!

Lurkin (*fiendish cackle*) Hee! Hee! Hee!

They stir up the audience, then go into a comic "nasty" duet and dance

Song 6

Bluebeard and Lurkin exit DL, *snarling and sneering at the audience. Marie creeps on* DR

Marie (*alarmed*) Ooh-la-la! Zey are going to poison zee guests! I must warn zem! (*She makes for the exit* DL)

Shivers suddenly appears DL

Marie halts in her tracks

Shivers Are you here again, girl! If you leave your post once more I will have you dismissed. Go back to the kitchens.

Marie (*timidly*) Oui, madame.

Marie scurries out DR. *Shivers glides out after her*

Ruby and Flora creep on DL. *They are now out of their travelling attire*

Flora (*in hushed tones*) It's very good of Robin and the others to keep a watch over us, but where on earth are we going to hide them in the castle?

Ruby Search me, Sis! We've got to get 'em *in* first!

Flora (*indicating* R) The main entrance is that way. Let's hope they're just waiting outside and we can slip them in without anyone seeing. (*She gives Ruby a gentle push*) Come on.

Ruby and Flora make for the exit DR

Shivers suddenly appears DR

Ruby and Flora retreat

Shivers (*gliding towards them*) Can I help you, miss?

Ruby (*stammering*) No! … Er … Yes! … Er …

Ruby pushes Flora in front of her

Flora (*to Shivers*) My sister and I were just having a look around the castle before dinner. Is that permitted?
Shivers Certainly, miss. The baron gave instructions that you are at liberty to enter all the rooms. (*Slight pause*). All, except the room in the Black Tower. That one is strictly out of bounds.
Flora Why?
Shivers I have no idea, miss. The baron alone keeps the key. I would be very pleased to show you the rest of the castle. (*To Ruby*) What can I show you first, miss?
Ruby The way out! … I mean … (*Spur of the moment*) The kitchen! (*Rambling on*) I like to see food! Yes! Eatin's a hobby of mine! I do it most days! (*Aside to Flora*) There's bound to be a back door we can let them in! (*To Shivers*) Yes! The kitchen! Take me to your larder!
Shivers Very good, miss. Please walk this way.

Shivers glides out DR

Ruby I'm sure she's on castors!

Ruby and Flora exit DR. *Bluebeard enters* DL, *followed by Rockbottom and Lurkin*

Bluebeard I trust your room is satisfactory?
Rockbottom Ay! Champion! Baron — er — about that thousand gold pieces …
Bluebeard Business later. First, may I offer you an aperitif?
Rockbottom A what?
Bluebeard Aperitif?
Rockbottom No, thanks. I've got me own! (*He shows his teeth*)
Bluebeard I mean a drink before dinner.
Rockbottom By gum! Now you're talkin'! Which way's t' bar?
Bluebeard No need. Lurkin!
Lurkin (*scuttling to his side*) Yes, master?
Bluebeard Go and prepare Mr Rockbottom one of our special cocktails. You know — (*unseen by Rockbottom he slips Lurkin the poison bottle*) — the one with the *extra* special ingredient!
Lurkin (*fiendishly*) Yes, master!

Lurkin scuttles out DL

Rockbottom A cocktail, eh? I've never 'ad one o' them things. I'm a pint o' wallop man misen.
Bluebeard Oh, you'll enjoy this.
Rockbottom Well, I'll try anythin' once!
Bluebeard (*aside*) That's all he'll *need* to do!

Lurkin enters DL. *He carries a large, smoking goblet*

Bluebeard Ah, here is it! (*To Lurkin*) I trust you've mixed it correctly?
Lurkin (*with a crafty wink*) Yes, master! Shaken and *none* stirred!
Bluebeard (*taking the goblet and holding it out to Rockbottom*) Here you are — a Castle Bluebeard Special. I guarantee that once you've tasted this you'll never drink anything else.

Lurkin suppresses ghoulish laughter

Rockbottom (*taking the goblet and blowing at the smoke*) Do I drink it, or send smoke signals? (*He raises the goblet to his lips. He pauses and sniffs it*) By 'eck! It's got a reight peculiar pong to it!
Bluebeard (*impatiently*) Drink up!

Rockbottom raises the goblet to his lips. Again he stops to sniff it

Rockbottom Er, I'm not so sure! (*To the audience*) D' you think I should drink it, folks?
Audience No!
Bluebeard }
Lurkin } (*together to audience*) Oh, yes he should!

A routine with the audience follows

During it, Marie enters DR, *with a sweeping broom. She takes in the situation, and pretends to sweep the floor, slowly working her way towards the others*

Rockbottom (*to the audience, curtailing the routine*) All reight! All reight! As I've drunk at the (*local pub*), I don't suppose it'll 'urt!

He raises the goblet to drink. Bluebeard and Lurkin watch with eager anticipation. By now Marie is sweeping right next to Rockbottom. She purposely bumps into him, causing him to spill the contents of the goblet over Lurkin

Marie Ooh! Pardon, monsieur! Pardon!

Bluebeard (*enraged, bellowing at her*) *You clumsy cretin! Get out!!*

Marie scuttles out DR

Rockbottom upturns the now-empty goblet

Bluebeard (*taking the goblet*) A thousand apologies, Rockbottom. (*Thrusting the goblet at Lurkin*) Go and prepare another!
Rockbottom (*hastily*) No, ta! Don't bother. I'll not chance it on an empty stomach.

Rockbottom makes a hasty exit DL

Bluebeard (*fuming*) Curse that clodhopping kitchen-maid! She ruined everything with her confounded clumsiness! (*To the audience*) But fear not, you puny peasants, the great Bluebeard is not beaten! I have another plan to rid myself of those two Rockbottoms! (*To Lurkin*) Have you got the toxic bane?
Lurkin No, master. It's just the way I'm standin'!
Bluebeard *The poison*, you idiot!

Lurkin gives him the poison bottle

Bluebeard (*to the audience*) At this very moment their dinner is being prepared in the castle kitchens. I shall go and add some ingredients of my own! (*He holds up the bottle*) Ha! Ha! Ha!

He sweeps out DR, *followed by Lurkin*

The Lights fade to Black-out. Music to cover the scene change

Scene 5

The castle kitchens

A back wall and side wings are painted to show a profusion of kitchen paraphernalia. Panto style, of course! A dresser with china, pots and pans, flour sacks, baskets of veg, haunches of meat, strings of sausages, etc. In the back wall, as high up as possible, is a practical window. There is a trick oven against the wings, UL. *There is a table* ULC, *set with the necessary props for a slapstick cake-making routine*

The Lights come up on Marie and the Chorus, as kitchen staff, cooks and maids, etc. Music. All is noise and bustle as they go about their various duties. This soon develops into a food-and-drink orientated song and dance number

Song 7

After the number, Shivers glides on L, *followed by Ruby and Flora*

At the sight of the housekeeper, the kitchen staff form a line across the stage and stand to attention

Shivers (*to Ruby and Flora*) These are the kitchen staff. Do you wish to inspect them?
Ruby What for — signs of life?
Shivers (*to the Staff*) Back to your duties!

The Chorus run out in various directions

Marie lingers. Shivers glares at her

Marie runs out R

Shivers glides over to watch her departure

The heads of Robin, Fetch and Carrie appear outside the window

Ruby sees them

Ruby (*yelling, pointing towards them*) Oooow!!

Shivers turns

At the same time, Robin, Fetch and Carrie duck from view

Following the direction of Ruby's still pointing finger, Shivers looks up at the window, then back at Ruby

Shivers (*gliding over*) Is something the matter, miss?
Ruby (*flustered, her arm frozen*) Eh?! … Er … No! (*Pointing her arm in another direction*) I — I was just admirin' that saucepan! Did you get it from Argos? (*She pulls her rigid arm down*)
Shivers If you have seen enough here, I will now show you the rest of the castle. (*She glides to exit* R)

Robin, Fetch and Carrie appear again

Ruby sees them, and nudges Flora. They both wave to Robin and the others. Shivers starts to turn

Robin, Fetch and Carrie duck from sight

Flora and Ruby quickly change their waves into wide, expansive gestures

Flora (*to Shivers*) We — we were just saying how *big* and *wide* this kitchen is! Not like ours at home.
Ruby No! Ours is so small we can only cook shortbread! (*Waving her arms about wildly*) There's *lots* an' *lots* of room 'ere!

Shivers gives Ruby a cold stare

Shivers Shall we move on? (*She glides towards the exit* R)
Flora (*stalling*) Er — no. We'd like to remain here. We'd like to stay and help prepare dinner. Wouldn't we, Ruby?
Ruby Yes … (*Double-take*) Eh?!
Flora Cooking is a great hobby of ours. Isn't it, Ruby?
Ruby What? … Oh, yes! Regular (*TV cookery show presenter*), we are!
Shivers It is not usual for guests to prepare their own food, miss.
Flora Oh, we don't mind a bit. We'll enjoy it. I'm sure Baron Bluebeard wants his guests to feel at home. So — you can leave us now.
Ruby Yes, get back to yer coffin — er — knittin'!
Shivers Well, I …
Flora and Ruby (*waving to her*) Bye! Bye!

Shivers glides out R. *Robin and Fetch and Carrie appear at the window*

Flora (*to Ruby*) Quick! You let them in, I'll keep watch in case she comes back!

Flora runs out R

Ruby goes up to the window and tries to reach the latch, but it's too high

Robin (*calling to her*) Find — something — to — stand — on!
Ruby (*not hearing and calling back*) I'll — find — something — to — stand — on!

Ruby looks about, then scuttles off UR. *Bluebeard and Lurkin enter* L, *gloating over the poison bottle. Robin, Fetch and Carrie duck out of sight. Ruby returns, carrying a small stepladder*

Completely unaware of the others' presence, she sets the ladder under the window and climbs up. Bluebeard and Lurkin watch in silence. Ruby opens the window and leans out with her bottom sticking up. Bluebeard indicates for Lurkin to investigate. He creeps across and eyes Ruby's wriggling bottom with a lecherous leer. He reaches up and squeezes her

Ruby (*yelling*) *Ahooow*!! Is that you, Flora!

Lurkin squeezes her again

Ahooow!! What are you … (*She comes out of the window and sees Lurkin*) *Waaaa*!! … (*She sees Bluebeard and gives him a soppy wave*) Yoo hoo!

Bluebeard (*moving over*) What are you doing? Why have you opened that window?

Ruby (*flustered*) Er — ur — *air*! I needed some *air*! It's very stuffy in 'ere! (*She waves her arms about and accidentally, on purpose, hits Lurkin. She comes down the ladder*)

Bluebeard (*suspiciously*) What are you *doing* in these kitchens anyway?

Flora enters R

Flora I can answer that, Baron. Ruby and I wish to assist in the preparation of dinner. I hope you have no objection.

Bluebeard (*turning on the oily charm*) Certainly not. Please feel free. What are you going to cook?

Flora
Ruby } (*together*) A pie! A cake!

Ruby
Flora } (*together*) A cake! A pie!

Ruby A cakey pie! It's an old (*local*) delicacy!

Bluebeard I see. Then I shall detain you no longer. Come, Lurkin.

Bluebeard and Lurkin move to exit L

(*Pausing for an aside to the audience*) I will return later and add a little something of my own! (*He shows the poison bottle*)

Bluebeard and Lurkin exit L, *gloating and cackling*

Flora Where are they?

Ruby I dunno! One minute they were outside, the next —— (*She stops short*)

Marie creeps on R

Marie (*in urgent, hushed tones*) Listen carefully. I will say zis only once. I come wiz a warning!
Ruby (*to Flora*) What is she — a cigarette packet?
Flora (*to Marie*) What's wrong?
Marie It is ze Baron! 'E is going to poi ——

Marie breaks off as she sees Shivers glide on L, *unseen by the other two. Marie dashes out* R

Shivers glides over to Ruby

Ruby (*calling after Marie*) Goin' *where*? (*Then to Flora, nonplussed*) Funny woman!

She turns and bumps into Shivers

Yaaaah!! Oh, don't creep up on me like that! Me whole life flashed before me! (*To the audience*) All twenty-five years of it!
Shivers I came to enquire if you have everything you need.
Ruby (*preening herself*) Well, I've 'ad no complaints so far! ... Oh, you mean for the cookin'! (*She goes up to the table and bangs things about*) Oh, yes! It's all 'ere!

Shivers glides out R

They watch her go

Robin, Fetch and Carrie appear at the open window

Robin (*loudly*) *Pssst*!!

Ruby jumps with fright

Flora (*rushing to the ladder*) Robin! Come in, quickly!

Robin climbs in and down the ladder. Fetch follows, then Carrie. Comic business with her getting stuck. Afterwards, Robin and Flora embrace

Ruby Oy! There's not time for that! We've got to find a place for you and Wallace an' Grommit to hide!
Robin This castle is huge. We're bound to find somewhere. Meanwhile, how about some sort of disguise?
Flora That's a good idea.

Ruby And I know the very thing!

Ruby dashes out R, *and returns immediately with three aprons and chef hats*

She distributes them to Robin and the others. Flora helps Robin. His hat and short apron fit perfectly. Comic business as Ruby helps Fetch and Carrie. Their aprons are much too long and their hats much too big, making them look ludicrous

There! If anyone asks we'll say you're outside caterers from (*local reference*)!

Robin You two stay here with Ruby. Flora and I'll go and find us a suitable hiding place.

Robin takes Flora's hand and they run out R

Ruby (*calling after them*) Mind ya do! No canoodlin' on the way!

Carrie is fiddling with her apron

(*To Carrie*) Stop playin' with yer pinny!

Carrie What'll we do if Bluebeard or someone comes in?

Ruby I've told 'im I'm gonna make some cakes. I suppose you two'd better 'elp me. Come on! Let's get mixin'!

They go to the table. A slapstick cake-making routine follows. (See the Production Notes on page x) It ends with Ruby putting the tray of hideous creations into the oven and turning it on

Bluebeard and Lurkin enter L

Ruby (*aside to Fetch and Carrie*) Look out! It's Bluebottle!

Fetch and Carrie quickly run out R

Ruby Ah! Your Baronfulness! You'll be very pleased to hear I've got one in the oven!

Bluebeard and Lurkin react

Cake!!

Bluebeard (*sniffing*) I — I can smell something!

Ruby (*indicating Lurkin*) It's 'im!
Lurkin No, it's not! (*He sniffs*) It's summit — burnin'!
Ruby *Me cakes*!!

She dashes up to the oven and throws open the door. Smoke billows out. She pulls out the cake tray. The mess has miraculously transformed into six delicious-looking little cakes! They are also very hot! Comic business as Ruby juggles with the tray, puts it on the table, and fans the cakes with a teacloth. Bluebeard brings Lurkin DR

Bluebeard Now's our chance! I'll keep her talking, while you poison the cakes!

He slips Lurkin the poison bottle and directs him L. *During the following, Lurkin creeps up behind the table to the cakes*

(*Addressing Ruby*) Miss Rockbottom! May I congratulate you on your culinary expertise.
Ruby (*coming* DR *to him, gushing*) Ta ever so muchly, thank you very kindly! (*She does an awkward curtsy*)

Lurkin is about to pour the poison over the cakes. The audience start shouting warnings

Ruby (*to the audience*) What's up wi' you lot?

Audience reaction. Lurkin ducks out of sight behind the table. Ruby looks upstage, then back to audience. Lurkin reappears

(*To the audience*) There's nobody there!

Lurkin is about to pour the poison. The audience continue shouting

(*To the audience*) All right! I'll look again!

Lurkin ducks out of sight. Ruby looks upstage, then back to the audience. Lurkin reappears

(*To the audience*) There's *still* nobody there! (*To Bluebeard*) What's the matter with 'em?
Bluebeard Take no notice! (*Snarling at the audience*) They're all stupid!

He stirs the audience up. During this, Lurkin pours the poison over the cakes. This done, he moves DL *and, unseen by Ruby, gives Bluebeard the thumbs-up sign*

Rockbottom enters L

Rockbottom Ay up! What's to do?
Bluebeard Ah! Rockbottom! (*He goes to him*) You are just in time to sample one of your daughter's excellent cakes! (*He leads him up to the table*)
Rockbottom Ee, by gum! They look good! Good enough to eat!
Bluebeard Then why don't you — *both* of you. (*He offers the tray*)
Rockbottom Ta! (*He takes the cake*)
Ruby (*taking a cake*) What about you an' Humpty! Aren't you gonna 'ave one?
Bluebeard Alas, no. Lurkin and I have just joined (*local Weight Watchers group*)
Rockbottom (*to Ruby*) Bon apertetee!
Ruby Bon Jovi!

They are just about to eat their cakes

Marie suddenly rushes on R

She appears to be in pursuit of an elusive fly, and is spraying the air with a huge aerosol can. She sprays around the others, making them cough and splutter

Marie (*to Bluebeard*) Pardon, Monsieur!! It is ze flies! We must not be 'avin' ze filthy flies in ze kitchen!

She sprays around Bluebeard, including the cake tray he is holding. She sprays around Ruby and Rockbottom, including their cakes. Still spraying, she rushes out R

Ruby (*recovering, and looking at their cakes in disgust*). Ugh! We can't eat these now! (*She takes Rockbottom's cake*) They're ruined! (*She takes the tray from Bluebeard*) All of 'em! I shall 'ave to throw the whole lot out!

She goes off UL, *with the tray of cakes. Still coughing and spluttering, Rockbottom exits* L

Bluebeard and Lurkin move downstage

Bluebeard (*to the audience, seething with rage*) Bah! Curse that clumsy maid! That's twice she's foiled my plans!
Lurkin Wot we gonna do now, master? (*He upturns the empty poison bottle*) Look! — All gone!

Bluebeard We shall now have to resort to a less sophisticated method of killing them!

Lurkin Y'mean ...? (*He draws his dagger with ghoulish glee, and makes throat slitting gestures*)

Bluebeard Yes!

Lurkin (*with devilish delight*) Ooo! Goody! — Shall I do it now, master?

Bluebeard No! Tonight — when they retire to bed! Come!

Sneering and snarling at the audience, they exit L. *Ruby returns and watches their departure. Robin and Flora creep on* R, *followed by Fetch and Carrie*

Robin (*to Ruby*) Pssst!

Ruby (*jumping with fright*) *Yaaah*!! Oh! (*Going to them*) Well? Did ya find a good 'idin' place?

Robin Yes. You've nothing to worry about with us keeping watch. (*Valiantly*) If Bluebeard tries anything, we'll be ready for him! (*He slaps his thigh*)

Fetch Ay! (*He slaps his thigh*)

Carrie Ay! (*She slaps her thigh and yelps with pain*) *Oow*! I shouldn't *do* that!

Ruby (*looking off* R) Look out! The kitchen staff are comin' back! Pretend to be workin'!

They rush to the table and pretend to be busy. Music

The Chorus and Dancers enter, and go straight into a lively song and dance

Song 8

Ruby and the others get caught up in the action and participate in the singing and dancing. The number ends with a tableau as ——

— *the* CURTAIN *falls*

ACT II

SCENE 1

The hall of Bluebeard's castle

The backcloth and side wings suggest a spacious room of fantastic design and bizarre décor. A rather unpleasant mixture of opulent oriental and British baronial. UC, *on a daïs, is a large, throne-like chair. Three smaller chairs are set near the* L *wings. Fetch and Carrie are concealed in two suits of armour at the back, one on each side of the large chair*

When the CURTAIN *rises, Bluebeard is seated on the chair* UC. *Lurkin is sitting at his feet. Ruby, Flora and Rockbottom are sitting on the chairs* L. *Shivers stands motionless beside Bluebeard's chair. The Chorus and Dancers, as colourfully clad troubadours, are entertaining the guests with song and dance. Robin is with them. He wears a very becoming troubadour costume and half mask. If desired, the number can include a speciality act*

The music changes, and the Chorus clear to R, *as Robin steps forward to sing. Comic business as he serenades Ruby, then turns his attention to Flora. He brings her to* C. *Still singing, and unseen by the others, he lifts his mask to reveal his face to Flora. They dance together as the others sing the refrain*

Song 9

After the number, Robin and Flora remain in each other's arms. Bluebeard rises and comes down to view the couple with suspicion. Sensing danger, Ruby jumps up, clapping wildly and pushing in between Robin and Flora

Ruby Bravo! Wonderful stuff! Bravo! (*Quick aside to Robin*) look out — there's a nasty about!

Bluebeard (*to Robin*) You, there! You're not one of my usual entertainers! Who are you? Remove that mask!

An awkward pause

Remove it, I say!

Ruby (*going to him*) Oh, Baron! You've seen enough of 'im! Yes!

Ruby pushes Robin towards the exit

Push off! An' stop 'oggin' the limelight!

Ruby pushes Robin off

Robin exits

(*Turning back to Bluebeard*). Why don't you let *me* entertain you!
Bluebeard You?
Ruby Yes! They don't call me the Martine McCutcheon of (*local place*) for nothin', y' know! I nearly got on "Sties in their eyes!"

She drags Bluebeard back to his chair and pushes him down

Now, you just sit on yer podium, an' I'll show you what I'm made of! (*To all, grandly*) I am goin' to entertain you with a little number entitled — (*chosen number*)! (*To the Chorus* R) Do any of you know it?

The Chorus shake their heads. Lurkin sidles down beside Ruby

Lurkin I do!

Shivers glides down to the other side of Ruby

Ruby (*reacting to him*) You would!
Shivers So do I.

Ruby reacts to Shivers

Ruby (*to the audience*) That's all I flippin' need! The Addams Family as a backin' group! (*To Lurkin*) You'll 'ave to sing *and* dance, y' know! How's yer arabesque?
Lurkin It was fine the last time I looked!

Ruby reacts

Ruby (*calling out front*) *Take it away!!*

Song 10

The choice of song and dance routine is left to the director. Perhaps a taped number with flashing disco lights? Whatever is chosen, it must give plenty of scope for comic capers. Lurkin is very energetic in his shambling way, and

Shivers has the ability to dance without appearing to move from the waist up! It ends with all three doing a high-kick finish

After the number, the Chorus applauds. Ruby is exhausted and has to be helped to a chair by Flora and Rockbottom. Bluebeard rises

Bluebeard (*to the Chorus*) Go!

The Chorus exit R

(*To the others*) I'm sure you must be exhausted after your day's exertions. I think you need some sleep.

Rockbottom Ay! Now you come to mention it — (*he yawns*) — I could do wi' some shut-eye! (*He yawns*)

Ruby (*yawning*) Me too!

Bluebeard Well, your beds await you. Good-night.

Ruby (*to Flora, rising*) Come on, Sis. Time for beddy-byes.

Bluebeard Ah! I would like Flora to remain here with me. For a *tête-à-tête*.

Ruby Does that mean cocoa an' bickies?

Bluebeard It means a private conversation! (*To Flora, with oily charm*) So that we can become better acquainted. (*To Rockbottom, pointedly*) That *was* the agreement — along with the thousand gold pieces.

Rockbottom Yes, Baron. (*He takes Flora aside, in hushed tones*) Stay an' 'ave a chat wi' 'im.

Flora (*with a grimace*) Must I?

Rockbottom Just to keep 'im sweet. Think o' the brass, lass!

Flora (*resigned*) Oh, very well! (*She goes and sits on the middle chair* L)

Bluebeard Shivers, show them to their rooms.

Shivers Yes, Baron. (*To the others*) Please walk this way.

Shivers glides out L. *Copying her, Ruby and Rockbottom glide out* L

Lurkin (*eager aside to Bluebeard*) Shall I go an' … ? (*He makes grisly throat-slitting gestures*)

Bluebeard (*aside to him*) Not yet! Have patience! Get out!

He pushes the disappointed Lurkin off R

Lurkin exits

Bluebeard turns and catches Flora's eye. He leers across at her, stroking his beard. With a shiver of disgust, she looks the other way

(*To the audience, with an evil chuckle*) Hee! Hee! Alone at last with the girl. Soon she will be in my power. She won't be able to resist my scintillating charm! Will she?

After byplay with the audience, he goes across and sits on the chair above Flora. She moves to the lower chair. He moves to the middle chair and leans in very close to her. Flora gets up suddenly, and crosses to C. *This causes Bluebeard to topple to the floor*

(*Getting up, and quickly regaining his oily charm*) There's no need to be shy, my dear. I realize you must be dazzled by my magnificence. All women are. But don't let that intimidate you. I am only a man for all that. (*He moves closer*) Come — show me a little affection! (*He puts his arm around her waist*)

Flora (*struggling*) How dare you! Let go of me!

Bluebeard (*holding her tighter*) Ha! Ha! I like a girl with spirit! It makes the chase worthwhile! Give me a kiss!

He tries to kiss her, while she tries to pull away. Suddenly, the two suits of armour become animated and walk forward with slow, clanking steps. They get level with the struggling couple, one on each side. They both wave their arms and emit ghoulish wails. Bluebeard sees them and releases Flora

Yelling in fright, Bluebeard runs out L

The suits of armour advance on the frightened Flora. When they get near to her, they both raise their helmet visors to reveal the smiling faces of Fetch and Carrie

Fetch
Carrie } (*together*) It's only me!

Flora (*relieved*) Fetch and Carrie! Thank goodness!

They both salute. Comic business with Carrie's arm getting stuck

Carrie Anyone got some WD40? I'm stuck!

Flora and Fetch pull the offending arm down

Robin, without the mask, rushes on R

Robin Flora! I thought I heard you calling for help. Are you all right?

Flora I am now. Thanks to these two.

Fetch and Carrie salute Robin. Repeat business of Carrie's arm getting stuck

Robin What happened?

Carrie Old Bluebeard tried to snog 'er!
Fetch But we scared him off!
Robin (*enraged*) That does it! I'm not hiding away any longer! I'm going to sort him out — right now! (*He strides to the exit* L)
Flora (*stopping him*) No, you mustn't! If he finds out you followed us here, he won't give father the money. It's only until tomorrow, then we can all go home. Please, Robin.
Robin Well — I suppose if you can endure it, so can I. Where's your father and Ruby?
Flora Gone to bed.
Robin Then I suggest you do the same. Don't worry. We'll still be keeping watch.

Fetch and Carrie salute. Carrie's arm gets stuck again. Robin and Flora embrace

Flora exits L. *Marie creeps on* R

Marie Pssst!!

They turn and see her. Fetch and Carrie panic, and crash into each other

(*Going to them*) Do not be afraid. I am 'ere to 'elp you.
Robin Who are you?
Marie My name is Marie. You are 'ere because of ze young woman, n'est-ce-pas?
Robin Yes, but ——
Marie I too am 'ere because of someone. My sister — Louise. Zare is no time to explain now. You must get ze young woman and 'er family away from 'ere at once! Already Bluebeard 'as tried to poison ze Papa and ze big sister!
Others (*aghast*) *What*!!
Marie Oui, but I — 'ow you say — *nibbled* 'im!
Others *Nobbled* him!
Marie Oui. You must get zem away from 'ere, before — (*looking off* L, *alarmed*) Mon Dieu! 'Ere comes ze 'orrible 'ousekeeper! You must 'ide!

Marie runs out R

Robin quickly hides behind the chair UC. *Panicking, Fetch and Carrie shut their visors and crash into each other. They just manage to freeze in peculiar attitudes*

Shivers glides on L

She crosses slowly in front of them, and they turn their bodies as she passes by. Sensing something, Shivers stops. Fetch and Carrie quickly jerk back and freeze

Shivers looks at them, shrugs and glides out R

They remain frozen. Robin emerges from hiding, and taps one of them on the helmet. They topple and crash into each other

Robin It's all right! She's gone!

They raise their visors

There's not a moment to lose! You heard what Marie said! We must get Flora and the others out of this castle at once! Come on!

They head for the exit L

Suddenly, Lurkin appears there, brandishing his dagger

Lurkin Ha! Ha! Goin' somewhere? I don't think so! (*Calling off* L) Master! Master! Come quickly! (*To the others, jabbing at them with his dagger*) Get back! Get back!

They retreat

Bluebeard rushes on L

Bluebeard What is going on? ... (*Seeing Fetch and Carrie and recoiling*) Ahh! The ghosts!!

Lurkin They ain't no ghosts, master. Look. It's just them two soppy servants. They must 'ave followed us back 'ere.

Bluebeard How did you get into my castle?

Robin Never mind that, Bluebeard! We're here to take the Rockbottoms away with us — now!

Bluebeard (*playing the innocent*) Do you mean my guests?

Robin (*with a scornful laugh*) Ha! Your guests! We know you've already tried to poison Mr Rockbottom and Ruby!

Bluebeard Me? No, I didn't!

Robin
Fetch
Carrie } (*together*) Oh, yes, you did!

They encourage the audience. "Oh, no, I didn't! /Oh, yes, you did!" routine with the audience follows

Bluebeard (*to the audience*) Silence! Shut up! (*To Robin, snarling*) What of it! What if I did try to kill them!
Robin Then you admit it?!
Bluebeard Yes! And I'll not fail the next time!
Robin There isn't going to be a next time! Your days are numbered, Bluebeard! As soon as we leave here, I'm going straight to the law!

Lurkin sneaks out L

Bluebeard (*airily*) Oh, really? And what makes you think you're going to leave?
Robin *You* can't stop us!

Robin, Fetch and Carrie advance towards Bluebeard

Bluebeard No, but I know a man who *can*!

Lurkin leaps on from L. *He is armed with a huge, fearsome-looking blunderbuss*

Cackling with devilish glee, he levels it at the others. They retreat, and Fetch and Carrie put their hands up

(*With a mocking laugh*) Ha! Ha! Ha! Try to leave, and Lurkin will blow you all to atoms! (*To the audience*) That goes for you as well! (*To Lurkin*) Take them to the dungeon and lock them up. I will decide how to dispose of them later. In the meantime, I have two other unwanted guests to take care of! Take them away!
Robin You won't get away with this, I'll … (*He advances*)
Lurkin (*pointing the blunderbuss at Robin*) Go on, punk — make my day!

Robin retreats

Move! (*He gestures with the blunderbuss towards the exit* R) *Move!!*

Robin, Fetch and Carrie exit R. *Cackling, Lurkin follows, covering them with the blunderbuss*

(*To the audience, as he goes*) Ooo! The power!

Lurkin exits

Bluebeard (*to the audience*) Ha! Ha! Ha! Those fools thought they could outsmart the mighty Baron Bluebeard! No-one can stop *me*! *No-one!!* Ha! Ha! Ha! (*Ad lib with the audience*)

Bluebeard exits L, *laughing and snarling at the audience*

The Lights fade to Black-out. Music to cover the scene change

SCENE 2

A passage in Bluebeard's castle

Tabs, or the same as Act I, Scene 4

Marie creeps on DL

Marie (*to the audience*) Ooh la la! I must try to get zem out of ze dungeon! But 'ow? ... 'Ow? (*She looks off* R) *Mon Dieu!* 'Ere comes ze 'orrible 'unchback! I will 'ide and zink of zomzin! (*She hides* DL)

Lurkin enters DR, *carrying a large key*

Lurkin (*to the audience, chuckling demonically*) Hee! Hee! Hee! That's them three safely locked up! (*He brandishes the key*) They won't be able to meddle in the master's plans no more! (*He hangs the keys on his belt*) I wonder what 'e's gonna do to 'em? (*With evil relish*) I 'ope it's summit *painful* an' *excruciatin*'! (*Ghoulish laugh*) Ha! Ha! Ha!

Marie comes forward, weeping pitifully. Lurkin reacts, and goes to her

Wos up wiv you?

Marie Oh, M'sieur Lurkin ... I am so un'appy! (*She sobs*) I 'ave ze mal du pays!

Lurkin (*taking a step back*) Ugh!!

Marie I am 'ome sick! I miss la belle France zo much! Ze boulevards! Ze cafés! Notre Dame!

Lurkin Notre Dame?! I got a cousin who works there! Per'aps you've seen 'im — 'angin' about! (*He does bell-ringing actions*)

Marie (*sighing with exaggerated fondness*) Ah, Paree! Paree! Where all ze men are so 'andsome and debonair!

Lurkin A bit like me, y' mean? (*He strikes his idea of a debonair pose*)

Marie (*grimacing to the audience, then carrying on, wistfully*) Ah! Zey are all so loving and romantic!

Lurkin Just like *moi!* (*He strikes his idea of a romantic pose*)

Marie gives another grimace to the audience

Marie Oui, Oui! Now zat I am looking at you, you are reminding me of Paree. (*She takes his arm and snuggles up to him*) Oh, merci, m'sieur Lurkin. You are zo kind.

She lays her head on his shoulder which he greatly enjoys

You are making me — 'ow you say? Chuck up?
Lurkin (*to the audience*) I fink she means — *cheer up.*
Marie (*to the audience*) No, she doesn't! (*Back to him*) Ah, oui! Cheer up! I am so cheered up, I am wanting to sing and dance! Voilà!

Song 11

Marie gives an O.T.T. rendering of a smouldering French song. (Not necessarily in *French, but it would be more effective if she could manage it!) During the song, she entwines herself around Lurkin and involves him in a comically seductive dance. He is spellbound. At one point, Marie stops singing and the music changes to an Apache dance. She proceeds to throw Lurkin about the stage. It then reverts back to the seductive dance and Marie resumes singing. During this, she is seen to surreptitiously remove the dungeon key from Lurkin's belt. The number ends with Marie bending Lurkin over in a passionate embrace, then letting him fall to the floor*

Marie runs out DR, *brandishing the key in triumph*

Lurkin clambers to his feet. Still mesmerized and enchanted, he dances around by himself, humming the refrain of Marie's song

Bluebeard enters DL, *and stands staring in disbelief*

Oblivious, Lurkin dances across and lays his head on Bluebeard's chest and closes his eyes

Lurkin (*cooing in an awful French accent*) *Oui, Cherie*? What ees it, my leetle French pastry? Tell your Lurky. Open up zem lovely lettle lippies! (*He reaches up and encounters the beard! He opens his eyes, gazes at it, then slowly looks up into the grim face of Bluebeard. He gulps and backs away*) S-sorry, master!
Bluebeard Have you locked up those meddling morons?
Lurkin (*back to his old grovelling self*) Yes, master.
Bluebeard Excellent! (*To the audience*) Then there is nothing to prevent us from disposing of those two rotten Rockbottoms! Ha! Ha! Ha! (*To Lurkin*) Have you got your dagger ready?

Lurkin (*drawing his dagger with devilish glee*) Yes, master!
Bluebeard Then let us get on with it!

Bluebeard and Lurkin exit DL, *laughing their evil laughs*

Marie creeps on from DR. *She beckons, and Robin enters, followed by Fetch and Carrie. They have removed their armour*

Robin Thanks for getting us out of the dungeon, Marie.
Fetch (*to the audience*) What's happening, folks?
Robin (*to the audience*) Have you seen Bluebeard?
Carrie (*to the audience*) What's he up to?
Audience He's gone to kill them! (*Etc.*)
Robin (*to the others*) You hear that! We've got to stop him before it's too late!
Marie I will show you ze way! Follow me!

Marie rushes out DL, *followed by Robin, Fetch and Carrie. Shivers glides on* DR, *and watches them go*

There is a flash of lightning and a roll of thunder

Shivers glides out DL

The Lights fade to Black-out. More thunder and lightning. Music to cover the scene change

Scene 3

Rockbottom's bedroom

An inset. A spooky-looking room with dark corners and cobwebs. Running down the centre of the room is a large, high bed. At its foot, facing the audience, is a large wooden chest. (See the Production Notes on page x). In the back wall, on each side of the bed, are practical archways. These are backed by a painted backcloth or black curtains

The Lights come up to give a creepy sinister effect

Rockbottom is in bed, fast asleep and snoring. He wears a nightshirt and tasselled nightcap

Thunder and lightning

Bluebeard's head appears around the R *arch. A second later, Lurkin's head appears on the same side, but much lower down. They tiptoe into the room*

Bluebeard (*in hushed tones, pointing to the bed*) Get on with it.
Lurkin (*hushed tones and drawing his dagger*) Yes, master.

Bluebeard creeps out through R *arch*

Lurkin goes to the bed, leans over Rockbottom and raises his dagger, about to strike. Thunder and lightning

Ruby (*off* L) Oooo! ... Daddy! Daddy!

Lurkin dives under the bed

Ruby rushes on from the L *arch. She is wearing an outrageous nightdress or ludicrous pyjamas. She has enormous curlers in her hair. She is very frightened and agitated*

(*Going straight to the bedside*) Ooow! D-Daddy! W-wake up!

Thunder and lightning. Ruby yells with fright and starts shaking Rockbottom

(*Yelling*) *Daddy!! Wake up!! Wake up!!*

Rockbottom wakes with a start and sits up

Rockbottom What the ... Ee up! ... What's goin' on? Ruby, lass! What's to do?
Ruby Oh, Daddy! I'm so frightened. It's all these terrible rumblin' noises!
Rockbottom Well, tha shouldn't eat so much! Go back to bed! (*He lies down*)

Thunder and lightning. Ruby yells and shakes Rockbottom again

(*Sitting up*) By 'eck! You are a big baby, our Ruby! It's only a bit o' thunder an' lightning! Act yer age, lass! Go back to bed!
Ruby (*trembling*) Y-y' know it scares me, Daddy! Can I come in with you, Daddy? Pleeeese, Daddy!
Rockbottom No, tha can't! Go back to yer own room! (*He lies down again*)

Very agitated, Ruby moves away to the far L. *Very loud thunder and a blinding flash of lightning. With a scream, Ruby runs across and leaps into the bed. This causes Rockbottom to be pushed out on to the floor. Annoyed, he climbs back in, and a battle for the bedclothes follows. Eventually, they both fall asleep and start snoring. Lurkin crawls from under the bed. He looks at the sleeping figures*

Lurkin (*to the audience*) Hee! Hee! Two birds with one stone! (*He leans over the bed with his dagger raised to strike*)

Thunder and lightning. Ruby wakes with a scream and sits up. Unseen, Lurkin dives under the bed

Ruby (*shaking him*) Daddy! Daddy! Wake up! It's no use. I can't sleep with all this lunder an' tightnin' goin' on. Read me a story, Daddy. Like you did when I was little.
Rockbottom (*sitting up*) *You? Little?* I can't remember back that far! No! (*He lies down again*)
Ruby Pleeese, Daddy. I've got a book in my room. I'll go and fetch it. Oh, pleeese, Daddy!
Rockbottom (*from the pillow, resigned*) Go on then.

Ruby gets out of bed and exits through the L *arch*

Rockbottom starts snoring. Lurkin emerges. He kneels on the bed and raises his dagger. Suddenly, Rockbottom gives a loud snort and rolls over to the left side of the bed. This causes Lurkin to topple and fall on to the bed with a muffled cry. He kneels up and raises his dagger again

Ruby enters from the L *arch, carrying a large bedtime story book*

Lurkin dives out of sight behind Rockbottom

Ruby (*as she enters*) Here it is, Daddy. I've got the book. It's got all my favourite stories in. (*She gets into bed*) Budge up a bit, Daddy!

She pushes Rockbottom over. Lurkin is pushed off the bed and lands on the floor. He crawls around and crouches in front of the chest. Meanwhile, Ruby is shaking Rockbottom awake

Wake up, Daddy! I've got the book! Wake up!

Rockbottom, half awake, sits up. Ruby thrusts the book at him

Rockbottom Eh? What ... Oh! (*He opens the book; reading*) "And they all lived happily ever after. The end." (*He prepares to lie down again*)

Ruby (*shaking him*) No, Daddy! You 'aven't read the rest of it yet! Start at the beginning! (*She stabs at the book*) There! There!
Rockbottom You're too old for this, Ruby!
Ruby (*bellowing*) *Read!!* (*She lies down*)

As soon as Rockbottom starts reading, Lurkin crawls around to Ruby's side of the bed and crouches there

Rockbottom (*reading*) "Once upon a time there lived a king who had three daughters. Their names were Josie, Posie and Rosie. Princess Rosie was very beautiful and ——"
Ruby (*suddenly sitting up*) Shh!
Rockbottom What?
Ruby I thought I could 'ear somethin'. It sounded like — heavy breathing!
Rockbottom That's just wishful thinkin' on your part. Now, do you want to 'ear this story or not?
Ruby Yes, but ——
Rockbottom (*pushing her down*) Then lie down an' sherup! (*Reading*) "Princess Rosie was very beautiful and everyone in the kingdom loved her. One day she was ——"
Ruby (*sitting up*) Shh!
Rockbottom Oh, what now?
Ruby I 'eard it again! (*Clinging to him*) T-there's something in 'ere with us, Daddy!
Rockbottom Rubbish, Ruby!
Ruby There *is*! (*To the audience*) Isn't there, folks?

Audience response

W-where is it?

Audience response

Which side? (*Pointing to* R)*That* side?

Audience response

(*Pointing to her* side) This side?

Audience response

Oooh! It would be!

With a grimace and without looking, she tentatively reaches out with her left hand to feel about. Comic business as she comes into contact with Lurkin's hair. She screams, and Lurkin dives under the bed. Ruby clings to Rockbottom

It's there! I felt it! — Somethin 'orrible an 'airy! It went under the bed! Get it out, Daddy! Get it out! (*She pulls the bedclothes over her head*)
Rockbottom (*disgruntled and getting out of bed*). It's probably just t' cat! (*He peers under the* R *side of the bed, then crawls under. Calling*) Puss! Come out, pussy!

Quickly Lurkin emerges and gets into the R *side of the bed, diving under the bedclothes. Slowly, Ruby uncovers her head*

Ruby (*to the lump beside her*) D-Daddy?
Rockbottom (*from under the bed*) Yes?
Ruby Did you find it?
Rockbottom No!
Ruby It must be there! Get out of bed and 'ave another look. (*Pushing the lump*) Go on, get out!

Rockbottom emerges from under the R *side of the bed and stands up. Ruby gapes at him, then at the lump beside her. Both yell with fright*

Ruby leaps out of bed and runs out through the L *arch, as Rockbottom runs out through the* R *arch*

Lurkin lowers the covers and peers about

He quickly crawls to the foot of the bed, opens the chest and disappears inside, closing the lid. Simultaneously, Ruby and Rockbottom peer nervously round their respective archways. They creep into the room

Rockbottom It's gone!

Both sigh with relief. Still shaken, they come and sit on the chest

Ruby (*still nervy*) What do you think it was, Daddy?
Rockbottom I dunno, lass. But, it's gone now.
Ruby (*looking about, scared*) I wonder where it went! (*To the audience*) Did you see where it went, kids?

Audience response

Rockbottom (*to the audience*) Where? In the box?

Ruby (*to the audience*) Which box? Y' mean *this* box?

Audience response

(*To Rockbottom, absently*) They say it's in the box we're sittin' on.
Rockbottom (*unconcerned*) Oh, *this* box.

A second for the penny to drop, then both jump up with a yell and run away to far L *and* R

(*To the audience*) Is it still in there?

Audience response

Ruby (*trembling*) Ooow! What we gonna do!
Rockbottom (*bracing himself*) I'm gonna take a look!
Ruby Oh, I don't think you should, Daddy! (*To the audience*) Do you?
Audience Yes!
Rockbottom (*taking a step towards the chest*) I'm not scared. I'm a Rockbottom!

Rockbottom steels himself, goes to the chest and throws open the lid. Both cower away, expecting something nasty to happen — but, nothing does. Rockbottom goes to the chest and looks inside

There's nowt there! It's empty!
Ruby (*going to look*) So it is!
Rockbottom (*indicating the audience*) That lot's playin' tricks on us! (*To the audience*) You're 'avin' us on, aren't ya?

Audience response

Oh, yes, you are!

A routine with the audience follows

Take no notice of them, Ruby. (*He shuts the lid of the chest*) C'mon, let's go back to bed and get some sleep! Just ignore that lot! (*Yawning, he climbs into bed and lies down on the* R *side*)
Ruby Yes, Daddy. (*Aside to the audience*) You'll still give us a shout if you see anythin', won't ya? (*She gives them a thumbs-up sign, gets into bed and lies down*)

Both start snoring. The lid of the chest slowly starts to open. The audience shouts warnings. Ruby wakes with a start and sits up. The chest lid closes

Eh! What! ... (*To the audience*) W-what is it?

Audience response. Ruby looks towards the chest

I can't see anythin'! There's nothin' there! Daddy's right. You're just playin' tricks! (*Yawning, she lies down and starts snoring*)

The chest lid starts to open again. The audience shouts but fails to wake the sleepers. The lid opens fully

Bluebeard emerges from the chest. He sneers at the audience, then shuts the lid. Rubbing his hands with eager anticipation, he moves to the R *side of the bed*

The sleepers snore loudly

Lurkin enters through the R *arch during the following*

Bluebeard (*reacting with rage*) Curses! Both sleeping like babies! What's that idiot doing! Where is he? (*Calling in hushed tones*) Lurkin! Lurkin!
Lurkin (*right behind Bluebeard*) Yes, master!
Bluebeard (*jumping with fright*) Ahh!!
Lurkin (*doing the same*) Ahh!!
Bluebeard (*cuffing Lurkin*) You fool! Why are they still alive? I told you to kill them!
Lurkin Well, I ——
Bluebeard No excuses! Do it now! I will stay here and make sure you do it properly this time! (*He pushes Lurkin towards the bed*)

Lurkin leans over the bed and raises his dagger, about to strike

Flora (*off* L, *calling*) Father? Father?

Bluebeard and Lurkin quickly dive under the R *side of the bed*

Flora appears in the L *arch. She wears a charming nightdress and robe*

(*Peering in*) Father? (*She approaches the bed*) Is everything all right? I've just been to Ruby's room and she's not there.

A loud snore from Ruby

(*Relieved*) Oh, she's here. (*To the audience*) I might have known. (*Moving down to the foot of the bed*) She's always been terrified of thunder and lightning. I can't say I blame her — not tonight. Especially being in this creepy old castle! (*She sits on the chest, facing front*)

During the following, silently, Bluebeard crawls from under the R *side of the bed. At the same time, Lurkin crawls from under the* L *side. They creep up on each side of Flora*

Flora I'd be feeling pretty scared myself if I didn't know that Robin and the others were keeping watch over us. But knowing that darling Robin is near at hand makes me feel very safe. Very safe indeed. (*She shuts her eyes and sighs blissfully*)
Lurkin (*to her*) Evenin'!

Flora reacts and jumps up. She backs away to R, *straight into Bluebeard's arms. They struggle*

Flora breaks free and runs out through the R *arch*

Bluebeard I'll go after *her*! You take care of *them*!

Bluebeard runs out through the R *arch*

Lurkin goes to Ruby's side of the bed. He raises his dagger, about to strike. Suddenly Ruby sits bolt upright. With closed eyes and arms stretched out in front of her, she gets out of bed and sleepwalks towards Lurkin. He backs away to the extreme L. *Just as she gets close to him, Ruby suddenly changes direction and sleepwalks to extreme* R. *Lurkin follows her with raised dagger. Ruby changes direction again and sleepwalks back towards him. He backs away. At* C, *Ruby stops and faces front. Lurkin creeps towards her with dagger raised to strike. Ruby suddenly turns and sleepwalks away to* R. *This causes Lurkin to almost topple over. Ruby sleepwalks about the room with Lurkin following her, and the stopping-and-toppling business is repeated. Finally, Ruby sleepwalks to* R, *and Lurkin crashes to the floor with a loud thud. This wakes Rockbottom, who sits up. Lurkin crawls out of sight to* L *of the chest. Ruby continues to sleepwalk* UR *and* DR

Rockbottom What the …? What's goin' on now?! (*He sees Ruby*) Ruby, what tha doin'? By gum! She's sleep walkin'! (*He gets out of bed and goes to her*) Ruby … (*He is about to touch her, then stops*) No! They say it's dangerous to wake 'em.

Ruby turns and sleepwalks out through the R *arch*

'Appen I'll follow 'er, to make sure she don't come to 'arm. Er! What a night!

Rockbottom goes out through the R *arch. Lurkin gets up and follows him out, with raised dagger*

Flora runs on through the L *arch. She is hotly pursued by Bluebeard*

Flora (*yelling as she goes*) *Robin! — Help me! — Robin*!!

Flora and Bluebeard run out through the R *arch. Robin runs on through the* L *arch. He is followed by Fetch, Carrie and Marie*

Robin I'm sure that was Flora calling for help! (*To Fetch*) You come with me! (*To Marie*) You go and wake Ruby! (*To Carrie*) You wake Mr Rockbottom!

Robin and Fetch run out through the R *arch. Marie runs out through the* L *arch*

In a panic, Carrie just runs up and down, then goes to the L *side of the bed*

Carrie (*coughing politely*) Ahhem! Wakey-wakey, Mr Rockbottom — Mr Rockbottom? (*She pokes the bed*) Crikey! Either 'e's lost some weight, or … (*She pulls back the bedclothes. Alarmed*) *'E's disappeared!* (*She backs away in horror*)

Marie runs on through the L *arch*

Marie and Carrie bump into each other and yell with fright

Marie Ruby is not in 'er bed!
Carrie Nor's Mr Rockbottom! I don't like this!

Flora screams loudly off stage

Carrie and Marie cling to each other

And I don't like *that* either!

They move down to below the chest

Marie Zis castle is a very strange place. In ze night I 'ave often felt ze disturbances.

Carrie It's probably the wind.
Marie Zey say it is — *'aunted*!
Carrie (*to the audience*) There's a surprise!
Marie 'Aunted by ze ghost of a mad monk!

Behind them, the chest opens and a tall, ghostly Shape rises up from inside the chest. It is draped in a long black monk's habit with a cowl that only partly conceals a gruesome skull face. It looms, motionless

Carrie (*scared, but trying to laugh it off*) A m-mad m-monk! Ghosts! Now you're just tryin' to scare me! There's no such thing as ghosts! (*To the audience*) Is there, folks?
Audience Yes!
Carrie Oh, no there isn't!

Routine with the audience

Well, I don't believe you! You'll be tellin' us next that there's one standin' right behind us!
Audience There is!
Carrie No, there isn't!

Routine with the audience

I don't believe it! And to prove it — we're gonna look!

Carrie and Marie slowly turn to look and the Shape raises its arm. They turn back to the audience, doing a silent scream

Finding their voices, Carrie and Marie yell and run out through the L *arch*

The Shape lowers its arm

Flora, still calling for help and being hotly pursued by Bluebeard, runs through the R *arch. They run past the Shape without seeing it and out through the* L *arch*

Robin runs on through the R *arch, followed by Fetch. They run past the Shape and out through the* L *arch*

Ruby, still sleepwalking, enters through the R *arch, followed by Rockbottom. They too pass the Shape without seeing it, and out through the* L *arch*

Lurkin runs on through the R *arch, with raised dagger*

Lurkin Where are they? (*He moves near to the Shape without seeing it*) Where are they? (*To the Shape, absently*) Which way did they go?

The Shape raises its left arm and points

Ta!

He makes for the L *arch, then stops in his tracks and looks back at the Shape. Yelling, he runs out through the* L *arch*

The Shape steps out of the chest and stretches its arms as if yawning. It goes to the bed, gets in and lies down

Flora, still yelling and pursued by Bluebeard, runs on through the L *arch and out through the* R *arch*

Robin and Fetch run on through the L *arch and out through the* R *arch*

Carrie and Marie timidly creep on through the L *arch*

Carrie (*looking towards chest, relieved*) Phew! It's gone!

The Shape sits bolt upright in the bed

Seeing it, Carrie and Marie scream and run out through the R *arch*

The Shape lies down again

Still sleepwalking, Ruby enters through the L *arch. She sleepwalks towards the bed, then changes direction and exits through the* R *arch. Out of puff, Rockbottom comes through the* L *arch. He sees the lump in the bed*

Rockbottom Thank goodness! She's gone back t' bed. (*He gets into bed and lies down next to the Shape*) By 'eck! Your feet's cold, Ruby! (*He falls asleep and starts snoring*)

Lurkin enters through the R *arch, and creeps to the bed*

Lurkin Ha! Ha! They've both gone back to bed! Now's me chance!

He raises his dagger, about to strike. Suddenly, the Shape sits bolt upright

Yelling, Lurkin runs out through the R *arch*

Rockbottom (*waking up*) Oh, flippin' 'eck! (*He sits up*) What's the matter with tha now, Ruby?

The Shape turns its grisly face towards Rockbottom

Rockbottom screams, leaps out of bed and runs out through the L *arch*

The Shape lies down again

Flora, still yelling and pursued by Bluebeard, runs through the R *arch and out through the* L *arch. Robin and Fetch run on through the* R *arch and out through the* L *arch. Carrie and Marie creep in timidly through the* R *arch*

Carrie (*to the audience, in hushed, frightened tones*) I-Is it still there?

The Shape sits bolt upright in the bed

Carrie and Marie see it, scream and run out through the L *arch*

The Shape lies down again

Flora creeps on backwards through the L *arch*

Flora (*to the audience, in a hushed tone*) I think I've given him the slip. (*She backs into the room, keeping watch on the the* L *arch)*

Bluebeard creeps on through the R *arch, and tiptoes towards her*

Flora backs straight into his waiting arms

Flora (*struggling*) Let me go! Let me go …!

Robin runs in through the L *arch*

Robin Flora!
Flora Robin!
Bluebeard You! How did you get ——?

Lurkin enters through L *arch, and creeps up behind Robin*

Robin Let her go at once, Bluebeard!
Bluebeard Never! *Seize him*!

Lurkin grabs Robin from behind and pins his arms

Laughing his evil laugh, Bluebeard drags Flora out through the R *arch*

Robin struggles to get free

Fetch, Carrie and Marie run on through the L *arch*

They rush to Robin's assistance. In a thrashing, tangled heap they fall to the floor. Lurkin manages to crawl from under the heap to DR *and stands up*

Lurkin (*in triumph*) Ha! Ha!

The others get to their feet. Fetch advances on Lurkin

Robin (*stopping him*) Never mind him! Bluebeard took Flora that way! (*He points to the* R *arch*) Let's get after them!

Robin and the others make for the R *arch, but Lurkin gets there before them and bars the way with his drawn dagger*

Lurkin Oh, no, you don't! You can't stop the master! (*Jabbing at them with dagger*) Get back! Get back!

Ruby, still sleepwalking, enters through the R *arch behind Lurkin*

He gets entangled in her outstretched arms

Robin, Fetch, Carrie and Marie seize the chance and run out through the R *arch*

Lurkin disentangles himself from Ruby and pushes her to the floor

Lurkin runs out through the R *arch*

The fall wakes Ruby, and she sits up and looks about her in a confused way

Ruby What am I ... ? Why am I ... ? How did I ... ? Huh! Daddy must 'ave pushed me out of bed! (*She gets up*) What a flippin' cheek! (*She gets into bed next to the Shape, but doesn't lie down*) Just for that, you can read me the rest of the story, Daddy!

No response. Without looking, she nudges the Shape

Daddy!

The Shape sits up. Both are facing front. Slowly, they both turn their heads and look at each other. Both scream loudly, the Shape giving a Banshee-like wail, and leap out of bed

Ruby runs through the R *arch, and the Shape through the* L *arch*

The Lights fade to Black-out. Thunder and lightning and music to cover the scene change

Scene 4

A passage in Bluebeard's castle

Tabs, or the frontcloth as used in Act II, Scene 2

Gloomy lighting comes up

There is thunder and lightning as Bluebeard enters DL, *dragging the struggling Flora behind him*

Flora (*pulling back*) Let me go! Let go of me!
Bluebeard Ha! Ha! Ha! Struggle all you want, you will never escape from me!
Flora Why are you treating me this way?
Bluebeard (*musing*) I thought you were different from all the rest, Flora. With them it was just a — financial arrangement. You were penniless, but, for the first time, that didn't matter to me. I admired you for yourself. Your charm — your grace — your beauty. (*Oily*) Come, it is not too late. We can still be — friends. (*He reaches up with his free hand to touch her face*)
Flora (*pulling back with revulsion*) Don't touch me, you loathsome creature!
Bluebeard (*with renewed menace*) So! You prefer to suffer the same fate as all the others!
Flora (*really frightened now*) Others? W-what do you mean?
Bluebeard Ha! Ha! You will soon find out! Come!

He drags her towards the DR *exit*

Flora Where are you taking me?
Bluebeard To a very *special* place! *My* special place! A place from which there is no return! I am taking you to — *The Black Tower*!

Very loud dramatic chords of music and roll of thunder

Laughing demonically, Bluebeard drags Flora out, DR

Thunder and lightning

Robin rushes on from DL, *followed by Fetch, Carrie and Marie*

Robin (*to the audience*) Have you seen Bluebeard?
Audience Yes!
Robin (*to the audience*) Has he got Flora with him?
Audience Yes!
Carrie (*to the audience*) Did she look happy?
Audience No!
Robin (*to the audience*) Where is he taking her?

Audience response. Loud dramatic chords and roll of thunder

Robin
Fetch
Carrie
Marie } (*yelling together, to the audience*) Where?!

Audience response. Loud dramatic chords and roll of thunder

Fetch (*to Carrie*) Did they say — *The Black Tower*?

Loud dramatic chords and roll of thunder

Carrie Yes, I'm sure they said — *The Black Tower*!

Loud dramatic chords and roll of thunder

Marie Mon dieu! Not — *Ze Black Tower*!

Loud dramatic chords and roll of thunder

Robin What is — *The Black Tower*?

Loud dramatic chords and roll of thunder

Carrie I dunno! But it sounds a pretty noisy place!
Marie Ze Black Tower is Bluebeard's secret domain in ze castle! No-one goes zare but 'im!
Robin Where is it?

Marie 'Igh up! On ze battlements! But you will not be able to enter! Zare is a door and only Bluebeard 'as ze key!
Robin Then I'll break the door down!
Marie Impossible! It is massive! It will take many more zan us to do it!
Carrie Specially with my bad shoulder!
Robin Then we'll need some help, but ——
Fetch I know! What about those villagers we saw dancing in the wood. They might help us. They're no friends of Bluebeard.
Carrie Dancers! I don't think they'll be much 'elp! (*She does mincing dance steps*)
Robin (*to Fetch*) It's worth a try! Get out through that kitchen window, and run to their village. Bring back as many as you can, and join us at — *The Black Tower*!

Loud dramatic chords and roll of thunder

Fetch Right!

Fetch runs out DL

Robin (*to the others*) Come on! (*He makes for the* DR *exit*)
Carrie Hey! You're forgettin' Mr Rockbottom and Ruby!
Robin So I am! Go and find them! Explain what's happening, and join us at ——
Robin / **Marie** } (*together*) — *Ze Black Tower*!

Loud dramatic chords and roll of thunder

Robin and Marie run out DR

Carrie (*to the audience*) Huh! Go and find 'em! I wish I'd kept me mouth shut now! I don't fancy goin' back into that spooky bedroom! Not with that mad monkey or whatever it is! (*She gulps*) Oh, well, 'ere goes! (*She creeps towards the* DL *exit, calling timidly*) Mr Rockbottom? Ruby? Mr —— !

Lurkin suddenly leaps on DL, *brandishing his dagger*

Carrie (*wailing*) *Oh, no!!*
Lurkin *Oh, yes!!*

Lurkin chases Carrie around and grabs her

Where are those meddlin' friends of yours? Tell me!

Carrie (*with bravado*) Nothing you can do will ever make me tell!

Lurkin thrusts the point of his dagger under her chin. She wilts

Except *that*! They've gone after Bluebeard! They've gone to — *the black dog*!

She looks towards the band/pianist, expecting the dramatic chords. Nothing

The black pudding?

Nothing

What's up! You gone on strike?
Lurkin I fink you mean — *The Black Tower*!

Loud dramatic chords and roll of thunder

Carrie That's it!
Lurkin Then I must go to my master's assistance! But first — *I'll dispose of you*!
Carrie Oh, no! Don't kill me before I've seen the next episode of (*TV serial or soap*)!
Lurkin Prepare to die! (*He raises his dagger*)

Shivers glides on suddenly DR

Shivers (*as she enters*) Lurkin!

This distracts Lurkin

Carrie breaks free and runs out DL

Shivers (*gliding towards him*) What is the meaning of this disturbance?
Lurkin Can't stop! The master needs me! I must go to — *The Black Tower*!

Loud dramatic chords and roll of thunder

With ghoulish laughter, Lurkin runs out DR

Shivers remains C, *facing front and motionless*

Ruby (*off* L, *calling*) Daddy?

Rockbottom (*off* R, *calling*) Ruby?
Ruby (*off* L) Daddy? Is that you?
Rockbottom (*off* R) Ay! Where are tha lass?

Rockbottom creeps on backwards DR. *At the same time, Ruby creeps on backwards* DL

Comic business as they both back into Shivers and react

Shivers Can I do anything for you, sir?
Rockbottom (*giving her a look*) I shouldn't think so!
Shivers Then if you will excuse me, I am wanted elsewhere.
Ruby The undertakers?
Shivers No, miss — *The Black Tower*!

Loud dramatic chords and roll of thunder. Rockbottom and Ruby react

Shivers glides out DL

Rockbottom Ruby, what's up wi' this place? I woke up and found misen sleepin' next to somethin' 'orrible! — I thought it were you!
Ruby Ditto, Daddy!
Rockbottom What's goin' on?
Ruby I wish I knew! Robin Reliant an' those two nitwits, Fetch an' Carrie, are supposed to be 'ere lookin' after us!
Rockbottom They're '*ere*? Why?
Ruby Because they thought old Bluebottle was plannin' something nasty! And I agree with 'em!
Rockbottom Rubbish, Ruby! T' Baron's all reight. 'E's gonna give me a thousand gold pieces in t' mornin'.

Carrie enters DL

Carrie Oh, no, he isn't! That was just a trick to get Miss Flora here. The old nasty wants her for himself. He even tried to poison you and Ruby, to get you out of the way!

The other two react

Ruby (*to the audience*) Is that true?
Audience Yes!
Ruby Honest?
Audience Yes!

Rockbottom (*enraged*) Why, the dirty, double crossin' ole ba — baron! Quick! Let's find Flora and get out of 'ere!
Carrie Too late! He's carried her off!
Rockbottom
Ruby } (*together*) Where?
Carrie He's taken her to — *the black hills of Dakota*!

Carrie looks towards band/pianist. Nothing

The Blackpool Illuminations? ... Oh! (*To the audience*) Where is it again?!

Audience response. Loud dramatic chords and roll of thunder

Carrie That's it! (*To the others*) Robin's already gone after them.
Rockbottom Then what are *we* waitin' for!
Ruby To the rescue!
Carrie
Rockbottom
Ruby } (*together*) To — *The Black Tower*!

Loud dramatic chords and roll of thunder

Carrie, Rockbottom and Ruby run out DR

Thunder and lightning, and the Lights fade to Black-out. More thunder and lightning, and music to cover the scene change

Scene 5

The Black Tower

An eerie eyrie, high up on the battlements of the castle. Prominent UR *is the grim façade of The Black Tower with its huge, solid-looking door. Battlements run across the back with a storm-filled sky beyond. There are stone wall wings with entrances* DR *and* L

As the Lights come up there is thunder and lightning. Ground mist swirls

To suitable music, the Dancers enter as bats and perform a wild and spooky dance

Song 12: Dance

The Dancers exit. Bluebeard enters L, *dragging a struggling and frightened Flora*

Bluebeard (*laughing his evil laugh*) Ha! Ha! Ha! Behold! — *The Black Tower*!

Loud dramatic chords and roll of thunder

Within its walls you shall suffer the same fate as many others! (*He produces a large key with his free hand*) Come, my dear! The Black Tower awaits you!

Thunder and lightning

Bluebeard drags Flora towards the tower. He unlocks the door and pushes her inside. Sneering at the audience and laughing, he follows her inside and locks the door

Robin and Marie creep on L

Marie (*pointing*) Zare it is! — *Ze Black Tower*!

Loud dramatic chords and roll of thunder

Robin (*to the audience*) Has Bluebeard taken Flora inside?
Audience Yes!

Robin rushes to the tower door and vainly tries to open it

Robin (*calling*) Flora! I'm here! Bluebeard! Open this door! Open it, I say! (*He hammers on the door*)
Marie (*going to him*) It is no use.
Robin (*looking up at the tower*) There must be another way in!
Marie Zare is not!
Robin There *must* be! I'm going to look around the other side! (*He rushes out* DR)
Marie Robin! Wait!

During the following, the tower door opens behind Marie, and Bluebeard appears

(*To the audience*) Oh, mon Dieu! 'E is wasting 'is time! Zare is no ossar way into ze tower. 'E should wait for ze ossars to come, and … ahhh!!!

Bluebeard grabs her and pushes her into the tower

Marie exits

Bluebeard locks the door and pockets the key

Lurkin enters L

Lurkin Master!
Bluebeard Shh! (*He points to off* DR)

Lurkin looks and gives an evil grin. He draws his dagger and makes for the DR *exit. Bluebeard pulls him back*

(*In hushed tones*) There's an easier way!

He pushes Lurkin L *and they conceal themselves in the shadows*

Robin enters DR

Robin (*as he enters*) I can't find a way in on that side … (*He looks about*) Marie? Where is she? Probably gone to find the others … (*He goes up to the tower door. Calling*) Don't worry, Flora, I'll soon have you out of there! (*He turns away*) We need to break this door down! What's keeping Fetch and those villagers? (*He goes up to the battlements and leans over*)

Bluebeard and Lurkin emerge, and creep up behind the unsuspecting Robin

Ah! There he is! (*Calling down*) Fetch! Fetch! Quick, bring them up! Hurry!

Bluebeard and Lurkin grab him

Bluebeard Throw him over!

A struggle, as they attempt to throw Robin over the battlements

Rockbottom, Ruby and Carrie run on L

They rush to Robin's assistance and pull him away to L. *Bluebeard and Lurkin clear to* R

Robin (*to the others*) He's locked Flora in that tower!

Bluebeard Ha! Ha! And you'll never see her again!

He and Lurkin rush to the exit DR

Fetch and several Villagers enter DR

Trapped, Bluebeard and Lurkin back away to UC, *near the battlements*

Robin Give me the key to that door, Bluebeard!
Bluebeard (*taking out the key and toying with it*) You mean — *this* key? This little key? (*Suddenly he throws it over the battlements*) Go and fetch it! Ha! Ha! Ha!

General uproar. Some rush to look over the battlements, while Robin and the others advance on Bluebeard

A figure (Shivers/Jemima) enters DL, *and stands motionless. It wears a long black cloak with a hood that conceals its face*

Carrie is the first to see it

Carrie (*yelling and pointing*) Agggh!! It's the mad monk!!

The others go silent and look towards the figure. It throws back the hood to reveal Shivers

Ruby Oh, no! It's Nightmare Nellie!

From under her cloak, Shivers/Jemima raises a pistol and points it in Ruby's direction. They react and release Bluebeard. He and Lurkin come down to Shivers

Bluebeard Excellent, Shivers! You're just in time. Cover those fools while I make my escape! Shoot *anyone* that attempts to follow me! (*Indicating the audience*) That includes *them*! Ha! Ha! Ha!

Bluebeard and Lurkin head for the DR *exit*

Shivers/Jemima (*pointing the pistol at him, in a completely altered voice*) Stay right where you are, Baron!

General reaction. Bluebeard stops and turns to see the gun levelled at him

Bluebeard What the ... ! What are you doing, Shivers?
Jemima The name is *not* Shivers! It's Blond! Jemima Blond! Special Agent!

The "James Bond Theme" is played. The others gasp as, with her free hand, Jemima whips off her Shivers' wig and shakes out a mane of luscious blonde hair. She throws off the cloak to reveal a very shapely figure clad in a slinky black catsuit and boots. She throws the wig and cloak into the wings, and strikes a pose. Reaction from the others. Cut the music

It was my assignment to investigate a series of disappearances around the world during the last few years. All the missing persons were female, and had one thing in common. They had all just married a mysterious nobleman who was visiting their country. In each case a very large sum of money had been paid to the nobleman as a marriage settlement. Straight after the wedding ceremony the money, the bride and the nobleman disappeared, and were never seen or heard of again!
Bluebeard (*sneering*) Very sad, but, what's it got to do with *me*?
Jemima All those noblemen had one thing in common. They all had—a blue beard!

General reaction

Eventually, I traced you to this castle and answered your advertisement for a housekeeper. (*In her Shivers' voice*) I knew a touch of the Hammer Horrors would appeal to you, sir! (*As herself*) All I had to do was wait. Sooner or later you'd give yourself away. And tonight, with the abduction of Flora Rockbottom, you did!
Robin She's locked in that tower!
Jemima (*moving to Bluebeard*) Open the door, Baron.
Bluebeard (*scoffing*) Ha! Impossible! The key now lies at the bottom of the castle moat!
Lurkin (*to Jemima, poking his tongue out*) Nah! So there! (*To Bluebeard*) Better not tell 'em you've got a spare one, Master — oops!
Bluebeard (*cuffing him*) You fool!
Jemima Give me that key. (*Putting the gun to Bluebeard's temple*) Now!

Scowling, Bluebeard produces the key and gives it to Jemima

(*To the others*) Someone take charge of these two, and don't let them get away.
Fetch
Carrie } (*together, rushing forward*) With pleasure!

They grab Bluebeard and Lurkin, and haul them away to DL. *Jemima goes to the tower, and unlocks the door*

Flora and Marie rush out

They run straight to Robin and the Rockbottoms. All eyes are on them

A Japanese lady emerges timidly from the tower, unseen by anyone

Ruby is the first to spot her

Ruby Hey! Look!

They all look towards the tower

A group of women (as many as you can muster!) follow the Japanese lady out of the tower in single file. They are all from different parts of the world and colourfully dressed accordingly. At the moment they are rather confused. The last to emerge is Louise, Marie's sister

Marie (*seeing her*) My sister! Louise!
Louise Marie!

They rush into each other's arms and jabber away excitedly in French. Jemima moves DR, *and surveys the group of women*

Jemima So! These must be the vanished brides! The brides of Bluebeard!
The Brides (*an angry cry*) *Bluebeard!!*

With enraged cries in many languages, the brides surge towards Bluebeard. They drag him downstage, where they kick and punch him until he falls to his knees. Ruby and the others cheer them on. At last, Jemima intervenes

Jemima (*pushing them back*) Ladies! Ladies! Control yourselves, please! I'd like to turn him over to your tender care, but unfortunately I can't. (*To Bluebeard*) On your feet!

Bluebeard stands up and nurses his wounds. Lurkin is pushed across to join Bluebeard

Bluebeard, you are under arrest on the charges of bigamy, fraud, kidnapping and attempted murder!

The others cheer

In due course you will stand trial, but in the meantime I need somewhere to lock you up.

Ruby And we know the very place! Let's put him in ——
Others — *The Black Tower*!

Loud dramatic chords and a roll of thunder

Jemima Of course! (*To Bluebeard*) Move!

She pushes him towards the tower. Fetch and Carrie push Lurkin

(*Pointing to the open doorway*) Get in!

Amid boos and jeers from the others, Bluebeard and Lurkin approach the doorway

Bluebeard (*pulling back*) No! You can't put me in there! It's atrocious! It's horrendous! It's inhumane!
Lurkin (*nestling up to him*) Don't worry, master. I'll be in there with you.
Bluebeard *That's what I meant*! (*He cuffs Lurkin*)
Lurkin (*gratified*) Oh, thank you, master!

Jemima pushes them inside and locks the door. All cheer. The Principals move forward

Ruby What a rotten, connivin' swindlin' old stinker *'e* was!
Rockbottom (*glumly*) Ay! Specially about that thousand gold pieces!
Marie (*going to Jemima with Louise*) I am sure Papa will reward you most 'andsomely for rescuing my sister.
Jemima Thank you, but I was only doing my job, and I can't accept a reward. Mr Rockbottom and his family might though.

Rockbottom pricks up his ears at this

After all, they did play a big part in helping to bring Bluebeard to justice.
Rockbottom That's true! (*To Marie*) D' you think your old man'll pay us a big reward?
Marie Oui!
Ruby (*getting an idea*) Hey! What about *that* lot? (*She indicates the brides*) D' you think their daddies'll cough up as well?
Marie Oh, certainement!
Ruby (*excited*) Oh, Daddy! You know what this means, don't ya?!
Rockbottom (*equally ecstatic*) Ay, lass! (*He throws his arms around Ruby and Flora*) The Rockbottoms 'ave got brass again! I'll be able to pay off all me debts, and reopen t' factory!

All cheer

Robin When you do, Mr Rockbottom, do you think you could give me a job?
Rockbottom Give you a *job*, lad? Certainly not!

Dismay from the others

As my future son-in-law I'm gonna make *you* a partner!

More cheering as Robin and Flora embrace, then everyone goes into a joyful song and dance, ending in a tableau

Song 13

After the number, a frontcloth is lowered or the tabs close

SCENE 6

Before We Go

Tabs or frontcloth. Bright lighting and bouncy music

Fetch and Carrie bounce on

Fetch (*waving to the audience*) Hallo, folks!
Carrie (*waving to the audience*) Hi, kids!
Fetch Well, that's it. It's nearly time to go.

They sigh and encourage the audience to join in a couple of times

Carrie (*to the audience*) Did you enjoy it?

By-play with the audience

What about that rotten old Bluebeard, eh? *All those wives!*
Fetch Yes! (*To a male in the audience*) Did I hear you say one was bad enough?

Ruby bounces on from one side, and crosses to the other, waving to the audience as she goes

Ruby (*waving*) Hallo! Hallo! (*Heading for the exit*) Goodbye!

Fetch (*stopping her*) Oy! You can't go yet!
Carrie (*indicating the audience*) No, we've got to let *them* do something they've been wantin' to do all night!
Ruby (*to the audience*) Ooo! You poor loves! Too much tea and lemonade, I expect! Well, just hold on for a wee while longer, and ——
Fetch No, not that! They all want to have a sing! (*To the audience*) Don't you?
Ruby Oh, goody! (*Or*) Well, you're goin' to! (*To Carrie*) Have you got the gubbins?
Carrie No, I always stand like this ... oh, y' mean the words! Here they come now!

The song sheet is lowered, or can be brought on by a couple of the brides

Song 14

They have fun getting the audience to sing along. Children from the audience can be brought on if desired and given sweets. Finally, the song sheet is removed, and the children return to their seats. Note: a raffle or some other routine could be substituted for a House Number

Ruby, Fetch and Carrie run out, waving goodbye to the audience

The Lights fade to Black-out. A fanfare

Scene 7

The Finale

This can be a special Finale setting or one of the previous full-stage scenes can be used

Bright lighting and bouncy music

All enter for the Finale walk-down. The last to enter are Robin and Flora

Robin The time has come for us to go.
Flora We hope you have enjoyed the show.
Rockbottom We'll get some brass! A tidy sum!
Ruby Look out, Harrods! 'Ere I come!
Fetch Now per'aps we'll get some wages!
Carrie Yeah! We ain't been paid for ages!

Jemima Bluebeard is off to a prison cell.
Marie I 'ope zey give 'im a shave as well!
Bluebeard (*to Lurkin*) *You* are to blame for this disaster! (*He cuffs Lurkin*)
Lurkin Not at all, but — (*he nestles up to Bluebeard*) thank you, master!
Ruby You've been a smashin' audience, not too strange or weird!
There's only one thing left to say ——
All (*waving*) Goodbye from — Old Bluebeard!

Finale Song 15 (or reprise)

CURTAIN

FURNITURE AND PROPERTY LIST

Further dressing may be added at the Director's discretion.

ACT I

Scene 1

On stage: Town backcloth
Town ground row
House flat with practical door
Town wings

Off stage: Carrier bags with items of comic clothing (**Ruby**)
Large laundry basket on wheels. *In it*: items of clothing (**Fetch** and **Carrie**)

Personal: **Butcher** and **Tradespeople**: long bills
Rockbottom: large bra, large sock down collar
Bluebeard: money bag with coins
Lurkin: dagger (carried throughout)

Scene 2

On stage: Tabs or frontcloth

Scene 3

On stage: Wood with castle backcloth
Foliage ground row
Tree wings

Off stage: Suitcases, bags, hat box, umbrella (**Ruby**)

Scene 4

On stage: Tabs or frontcloth

Off stage: Suitcases, bags, etc. (**Ruby**)
Smoking goblet (**Lurkin**)
Broom (**Marie**)

Personal: **Bluebeard**: poison bottle

SCENE 5

On stage: Kitchen back wall with practical window
Kitchen wings
Trick oven. *In it*: six delicious-looking little cakes on a tray
Table. *On it*: cake-making equipment and ingredients for slapstick routine

Off stage: Small stepladder (**Ruby**)
Three aprons and chefs' hats (**Ruby**)
Huge aerosol can (**Marie**)

Personal: **Bluebeard**: poison bottle

ACT II

SCENE 1

On stage: Hall backcloth
Hall wings
Daïs with throne-like chair
Three smaller chairs

Off stage: Large blunderbuss (**Lurkin**)

Personal: **Robin**: mask

SCENE 2

On stage: Tabs or frontcloth

Off stage: Large key (**Lurkin**)

SCENE 3

On stage: Stone back wall with two practical archways
Painted backcloth or black curtains as backing
Stone wings
Double bed. *On it*: sheets, pillows, blankets, etc.
Large chest (practical)

Off stage: Large bedtime story book (**Ruby**)

SCENE 4

On stage: Tabs or frontcloth

SCENE 5

On stage: Stormy sky backcloth
Battlements
Stone wings
Tower piece with practical door

Personal: **Bluebeard**: two large keys
Shivers: pistol

SCENE 6

On stage: Tabs or frontcloth

Off stage: Song sheet (**Stage Management or Chorus**)
Sweets for children in audience (**Ruby, Fetch** and **Carrie**)

SCENE 7

On stage: Finale, special setting or one of the full stage scenes can be used

LIGHTING PLOT

Property fittings required: nil
Various interior and exterior settings

ACT 1, SCENE 1

To open: General exterior lighting

Cue 1	**Robin** and **Flora** sing Song 2 *Romantic lighting with follow spot*	(Page 3)
Cue 2	End of Song 2 *Take out spot, return to previous lighting*	(Page 3)
Cue 3	**Ruby**: "I'm just minglin' with the masses!" *Follow spot on* **Ruby**, *or bring up house lights*	(Page 3)
Cue 4	**Ruby** gets on to the stage *Take out spot, or take out house lights*	(Page 3)
Cue 5	**Ruby**: " — and *I'm desperate!*" *Follow spot*	(Page 4)
Cue 6	End of Song 3 *Take out spot*	(Page 4)
Cue 7	**Carrie**: "... every silver cloud has a torn lining!" *Follow spot for Song 4*	(Page 6)
Cue 8	End of Song 4 *Take out spot*	(Page 6)
Cue 9	**Fetch and Carrie** exit with basket *Dim general lighting. "Sinister" follow spot on* **Bluebeard**	(Page 8)
Cue 10	**Ruby** enters *Take out spot and return to previous lighting*	(Page 9)
Cue 11	End of Reprise of Song 1 *Fade lights to black-out*	(Page 14)

ACT I, Scene 2

To open: General interior lighting

Cue 12	**Fetch and Carrie** exit *Fade lights to black-out*	(Page 19)

ACT I, Scene 3

To open: General woodland lighting

Cue 13	End of reprise of Song 5 *Fade lights to black-out*	(Page 24)

ACT I, Scene 4

To open: Gloomy, sinister interior lighting

Cue 14	**Lurkin** "Hee! Hee! Hee!" *Follow spot for Song 6*	(Page 26)
Cue 15	End of Song 6 *Take out spot and return to previous lighting*	(Page 26)
Cue 16	**Bluebeard** and **Lurkin** exit *Fade lights to black-out*	(Page 29)

ACT I, Scene 5

To open: General interior lighting

No cues

ACT II, Scene 1

To open: General interior lighting

Cue 17	**Robin** sings duet with **Flora** *Romantic lighting and follow spot*	(Page 38)
Cue 18	End of Song 9 *Take out spot and return to previous lighting*	(Page 38)

Cue 19 **Ruby**: " Take it away!" (Page 39)
Special lighting for Song 10

Cue 20 End of Song 10 (Page 40)
Return to previous lighting

Cue 21 **Bluebeard** exits (Page 45)
Fade lights to black-out

ACT II, SCENE 2

To open: Gloomy interior lighting

Cue 22 **Marie**: "Voilà!" (Page 46)
Brighten general lighting and follow spot for Song 11

Cue 23 End of Song 11 (Page 46)
Take out spot and return to previous lighting

Cue 24 **Shivers** enters (Page 47)
Flash of lightning

Cue 25 **Shivers** exits (Page 47)
Fade lights to black-out, then flash of lightning

ACT II, SCENE 3

To open: Creepy, sinister interior lighting. Flash of lightning

Cue 26 **Lurkin** raises his dagger (Page 48)
Flash of lightning

Cue 27 **Ruby**: "Oow! D … Daddy! — Wake up!" (Page 48)
Flash of lightning

Cue 28 **Rockbottom**: " Go back to bed!" (Page 48)
Flash of lightning

Cue 29 **Ruby** moves away from the bed to the far L (Page 48)
Flash of lightning

Cue 30 **Lurkin** raises his dagger (Page 49)
Flash of lightning

Cue 31 **Marie**: "Zey say it is — 'aunted!" (Page 56)
Dim out general lighting. Sinister follow spot on **The Shape** *as it emerges from chest*

Cue 32 **The Shape** gets into bed and lies down (Page 57)
Take out spot and return to previous lighting

Cue 33 **The Shape** and **Ruby** run out (Page 60)
Flash of lightning, then fade lights to black-out

ACT II, Scene 4

To open: Gloomy interior lighting

Cue 34 **Bluebeard** and **Flora** enter (Page 60)
Flash of lightning

Cue 35 **Bluebeard** and **Flora** exit (Page 61)
Flash of lightning

Cue 36 **Ruby, Rockbottom, Carrie** exit (Page 65)
Flash of lightning, then fade lights to black-out

ACT II, Scene 5

To open: Sinister exterior lighting. Flash of lightning

Cue 37 Special lighting for Song 12: Dance (Page 65)

Cue 38 End of Song 12: Dance (Page 65)
Return to previous lighting

Cue 39 **Bluebeard**: "The Black Tower awaits you!' (Page 66)
Flash of lightning

Cue 40 **Robin** and **Flora** embrace (Page 72)
Brighten general lighting

ACT II, Scene 6

To open: Bright general lighting

Cue 41 **Carrie**: "Here they come now!" (Page 73)
Bring up house lights. Spot on song sheet

Cue 42 **Children** return to audience (Page 73)
Take out house lights. Take out spot

Cue 43 **Ruby, Fetch, Carrie** exit (Page 73)
Fade lights to black-out

ACT II, SCENE 7 (FINALE)

To open: Bright general lighting

EFFECTS PLOT

ACT I

Cue 1	**Ruby** opens oven door *Smoke billows from oven*	(Page 35)

ACT II

Cue 2	**Ruby**: "Take it away!" *Taped music for Song 10 (optional)*	(Page 39)
Cue 3	**Shivers** enters *Thunder*	(Page 47)
Cue 4	**Shivers** exits *Thunder*	(Page 47)
Cue 5	To open Scene 3 *Thunder*	(Page 47)
Cue 6	**Lurkin** raises his dagger *Thunder*	(Page 48)
Cue 7	**Ruby**: "Ooow! D — Daddy! W — Wake up!" *Thunder*	(Page 48)
Cue 8	**Rockbottom**: "Go back to bed!" *Thunder*	(Page 48)
Cue 9	**Ruby** moves away from the bed to the far L *Thunder*	(Page 48)
Cue 10	**Lurkin** raises his dagger *Thunder*	(Page 49)
Cue 11	**The Shape** and **Ruby** run out *Thunder*	(Page 60)
Cue 12	**Bluebeard** and **Flora** enter *Thunder*	(Page 60)

Cue 13	**Bluebeard:** "... *The Black Tower!*" *Thunder*	(Page 60)
Cue 14	**Bluebeard** and **Flora** exit *Thunder*	(Page 60)
Cue 15	**Robin**: "Where is he taking her?" *Thunder*	
Cue 16	**Robin/Fetch/Carrie/Marie**: "Where?" *Thunder*	(Page 61)
Cue 17	**Fetch**: "... *The Black Tower?*" *Thunder*	(Page 61)
Cue 18	**Carrie** : "... *The Black Tower!*" *Thunder*	(Page 61)
Cue 19	**Marie**: " ... *Ze Black Tower!*" *Thunder*	(Page 61)
Cue 20	**Robin**: "... *The Black Tower?*" *Thunder*	(Page 61)
Cue 21	**Robin**: "... *The Black Tower!*" *Thunder*	(Page 62)
Cue 22	**Robin** and **Marie** : " ... *Ze Black Tower!*" *Thunder*	(Page 62)
Cue 23	**Lurkin** : "... *The Black Tower!*" *Thunder*	(Page 63)
Cue 24	**Lurkin** : "... *The Black Tower!*" *Thunder*	(Page 63)
Cue 25	**Shivers** : "... *The Black Tower!*" *Thunder*	(Page 64)
Cue 26	**Audience** : "... *The Black Tower!*" *Thunder*	(Page 65)
Cue 27	**Ruby/Rockbottom/Carrie** : "... *The Black Tower!*" *Thunder*	(Page 65)
Cue 28	To open Scene 5 *Ground mist and thunder*	(Page 65)

Cue 29	**Bluebeard** : "... *The Black Tower!*" *Thunder*	(Page 66)
Cue 30	**Bluebeard**: "... *The Black Tower awaits you!*" *Thunder*	(Page 66)
Cue 31	**Marie**: " ... *Ze Black Tower!*" *Thunder*	(Page 66)
Cue 32	**All**: "... *The Black Tower!*" *Thunder*	(Page 71)

COPYRIGHT MUSIC

The notice printed below on behalf of the Performing Right Society should be carefully read if any other copyright music is used in this play.

The permission of the owner of the performing rights in copyright music must be obtained before any public performance may be given, whether in conjunction with a play or sketch or otherwise, and this permission is just as necessary for amateur performances as for professional. The majority of copyright musical works (other than oratorios, musical plays and similar dramatico-musical works) are controlled in the British Commonwealth by the PERFORMING RIGHT SOCIETY LTD, 29-33 Berners Street, London W1P 4AA.

The Society's practice is to issue licences authorizing the use of its repertoire to the proprietors of premises at which music is publicly performed, or, alternatively, to the organizers of musical entertainments, but the Society does not require payment of fees by performers as such. Producers or promoters of plays, sketches, etc., at which music is to be performed, during or after the play or sketch, should ascertain whether the premises at which their performances are to be given are covered by a licence issued by the Society, and if they are not, should make application to the Society for particulars as to the fee payable.

A separate and additional licence from PHONOGRAPHIC PERFORMANCES LTD, 1 Upper James Street, London W1R 3HG, is needed whenever commercial recordings are used.